An Introduction to Green Process Management

Also available from ASQ Quality Press:

ISO 26000:2010: Guidance on social responsibility
ISO

Corporate Sustainability Planning Assessment Guide: A Comprehensive Organizational Assessment
Donald C. Fisher

Transactional Six Sigma for Green Belts: Maximizing Service and Manufacturing Processes
Samuel E. Windsor

ANSI/ISO/ASQ E14001-2004: Environmental management systems— Requirements with guidance for use
ANSI/ISO/ASQ

The Certified Six Sigma Green Belt Handbook
Roderick A. Munro, Matthew J. Maio, Mohamed B. Nawaz, Govindarajan Ramu, and Daniel J. Zrymiak

The Quality Toolbox, Second Edition
Nancy R. Tague

The Certified Manager of Quality/Organizational Excellence Handbook, Third Edition
Russell T. Westcott, editor

The Certified Six Sigma Black Belt Handbook, Second Edition
T. M. Kubiak and Donald W. Benbow

The Certified Quality Engineer Handbook, Third Edition
Connie M. Borror, editor

ISO 9001:2008 Internal Audits Made Easy: Tools, Techniques, and Step-by-Step Guidelines for Successful Internal Audits, Third Edition
Ann W. Phillips

Root Cause Analysis: Simplified Tools and Techniques, Second Edition
Bjørn Andersen and Tom Fagerhaug

Enabling Excellence: The Seven Elements Essential to Achieving Competitive Advantage
Timothy A. Pine

To request a complimentary catalog of ASQ Quality Press publications, call 800-248-1946, or visit our Web site at www.asq.org/quality-press.

An Introduction to Green Process Management

Sam Windsor

ASQ Quality Press
Milwaukee, Wisconsin

American Society for Quality, Quality Press, Milwaukee 53203
© 2011 by ASQ
All rights reserved. Published 2010
Printed in the United States of America
16 15 14 13 12 11 10   5 4 3 2 1

Library of Congress Cataloging-in-Publication Data

Windsor, Samuel E., 1962–
  An introduction to green process management / Sam Windsor.
    p. cm.
  Includes bibliographical references and index.
  ISBN 978-0-87389-791-4 (soft cover : alk. paper)
  1. Green products. 2. Green marketing. 3. Green movement. 4. Sustainable living.
  I. Title.

  HF5413.W56 2010
  658.4'083—dc22   2010027466

ISBN: 978-0-87389-791-4

Publisher: William A. Tony
Acquisitions Editor: Matt T. Meinholz
Project Editor: Paul O'Mara
Production Administrator: Randall Benson

ASQ Mission: The American Society for Quality advances individual, organizational,
and community excellence worldwide through learning, quality improvement, and
knowledge exchange.

Attention Bookstores, Wholesalers, Schools, and Corporations: ASQ Quality Press
books, video, audio, and software are available at quantity discounts with bulk
purchases for business, educational, or instructional use. For information, please
contact ASQ Quality Press at 800-248-1946, or write to ASQ Quality Press,
P.O. Box 3005, Milwaukee, WI 53201-3005.

To place orders or to request ASQ membership information, call 800-248-1946. Visit our
Web site at www.asq.org/quality-press.

  Printed on acid-free paper

Quality Press
600 N. Plankinton Avenue
Milwaukee, Wisconsin 53203
Call toll free 800-248-1946
Fax 414-272-1734
www.asq.org
http://www.asq.org/quality-press
http://standardsgroup.asq.org
E-mail: authors@asq.org

Table of Contents

List of Figures and Tables

Acknowledgments

As has been said many times, no book is the work of one person. When you write a book you depend on the honest feedback of your friends. This book is no different; I would like to thank my long-time friend and business partner Kevin Waddell of Innovation Quality Services for his content contributions, input, and honest feedback. Many thanks also go to Lou Anne Banks for editing and asking me "what do you mean by this?" many, many times.

To complete an undertaking such as a book, the support of your family can never be overestimated, and for that support my thanks go out to my wife Tammy and son Nicholas. Their encouragement and support has been the driving force throughout my career.

Preface

BP appears to have made multiple decisions for economic reasons that increased the danger of a catastrophic well failure. In several instances, these decisions appear to violate industry guidelines and were made despite warnings from BP's own personnel and its contractors. In effect, it appears that BP repeatedly chose risky procedures in order to reduce costs and save time and made minimal efforts to contain the added risk.

—Excerpt from letter dated June 14, 2010
from U.S. Representatives Henry Waxman
and Bart Stupak to BP CEO Tony Hayward

The BP oil spill that occurred as a result of an explosion on the Deepwater Horizon drill rig on May 19, 2010, will forever link BP's company name to an environmental disaster much like the *Exxon Valdez* or Union Carbide's Bhopal disaster. BP's value as a company has sharply dropped, and consumers are calling for boycotts on BP's products.

This event is clear evidence of the link between a company's reputation and it's environmental performance. While it does not prove that being green will save your business, it does show that being seen as a company that is not environmentally friendly will have an impact on your business. The excerpt above may be seen as political but it should also be seen as further evidence of the continuing emphasis on the environment and corporate responsibility as it relates to the environment. No company would want a letter from congress accusing them of taking shortcuts that endangered human life or the environment.

This book didn't start as a book. It started as a quest to understand what *green* really meant after I was given an assignment to lead the effort to become a "green" company. This task was given to me because of the growing attention to the environment in the business world, and to better manage and present the business to the marketplace as an environmentally friendly company.

The first challenge in becoming a green company was to understand what a green company actually is. I approached this task with my background in management and process improvement, and searched for tangible ways to define and measure "green." I searched the Internet, read books, and reviewed news articles. I was looking for a clear definition of green and how to go about creating a green company. What I found was a confusing mass of information that included carbon credits, green product certifications, various environmental standards, and methods to address environmental impacts, along with numerous descriptions and claims on how to be green and environmentally friendly. This mass of information left me more confused than before. It seemed that everyone had a different approach and definition of what green meant. To some, green simply meant recycling, or maybe using a renewable energy source; others claimed that becoming certified to a standard meant they were green. One common theme was the idea of measuring and reducing carbon emissions and the concept of being something called *carbon neutral*.

I soon realized that everything a person or business does has some sort of impact on the environment. So I wondered how anyone or anything could really be green. These questions led me to more research. The research led to theories, the theories to participation in a national trade association, and participation to presentations on the subject. Those presentations finally spawned a book. During the writing of this book I realized how political green has become, especially when it comes to measuring carbon emissions.

The intent of this book is to give interested parties an overview of green and its impact on business without spending countless hours researching the subject. It provides information in a manner that can be used to help businesses determine the role green will play in their futures. The book is not intended as a detailed implementation guide, but as an aid in understanding the current thinking on what green really is and what an organization can do.

The political aspects of green and carbon emissions are mentioned not to take sides or to promote an agenda, but to help give the reader a better understanding of how green may or may not be perceived by customers.

The book is presented in three major sections. The first section is intended to give an overall understanding of what is meant by green, a brief history of the environmental movement as it relates to business, trends in carbon measuring and reporting, and definitions of green. The second section discusses standards, certifications, and measurements that relate to green and environmental management. The final section presents methods that may be used to implement and manage green processes within an organization, along with tools and a road map that may be used by those companies seeking to become green. The road map utilizes process improvement tools that will be familiar to many organizations.

Section 1
Understanding Green

When I was growing up, if someone said something was "green," you knew it was green and not blue, yellow, or some other color. But green isn't just a color anymore. Everything is green. Energy is green, household cleaners are green, buildings are green, and so many other things are green. Do we really know what green is or isn't anymore?

Green is all over the news, featured in advertising and used as a marketing tool by both the public and private sectors. We talk about green jobs, becoming green, recycling, and carbon offsetting. Companies have "greener products" and politicians have green platforms.

No matter what happens in Washington with the various versions of the climate bill, or what your politics are concerning green and global warming, it is clear that "green" will be around for some time. Like any other factor in business, green should be addressed, and its opportunities evaluated.

A LOOK AT THE GREEN REVOLUTION

If a man walks in the woods for love of them half of
each day, he is in danger of being regarded as a loafer;
but if he spends his whole day as a speculator, shearing
off those woods and making earth bald before her time,
he is esteemed an industrious and enterprising citizen.

—Henry David Thoreau,
Walden and *Life Without Principle*

Industry by its very nature converts natural resources into products and services for consumption. This puts business and the jobs business provides at odds with the environment.

Some of the earliest efforts by environmentalists focused on preserving land and forests. The rapid expansion of the American industrial revolution in the late 1800s created these concerns. People saw the natural lands disappearing to farming, mining, and lumbering. At the same time, smoke from factories and steel mills began to fill the air. With cities expanding, early concern may have been more for a spot to take a vacation than for preserving the planet. Regardless of the reason, a tug of war emerged between the industries that provided jobs and the environmentalists who grew increasingly concerned about preservation.

Some say Henry David Thoreau was the first environmentalist; some say it was Teddy Roosevelt or maybe even John Muir. For the purpose of this discussion, it really doesn't matter. What matters to business is that around the end of the nineteenth century, just as the country was becoming an industrial superpower, there were already people keeping their eyes on what business was doing and evaluating the impact companies were having on the environment.

Yosemite was created as a state park in 1864 (see Figure 1). The word "ecology" was coined shortly after. Soon, early environmentalists started to recognize the need to preserve forests and other lands for future generations. The National Park Service was founded in 1916.

John Muir, the first president of the Sierra Club and champion of efforts to preserve natural lands, took his environmental efforts into the political arena. Muir continuously wrote articles that brought attention to how the land and forests were abused for economic purposes. In 1903, during a visit to Yosemite with President Theodore Roosevelt, Muir convinced the president to return parts of Yosemite that were used for commercial purposes to the federal government for protection. The interaction of business, politics, and environmental activism began to shape the way businesses are run today.

The United States soon realized the highs of the 1920s, the lows of the 1930s, and war in the 1940s. Although there were early champions of the environment such as Aldo Leopold, considered the father of wildlife management and an early leader in the newly formed U.S. Forest Service, actions during the 1920s and 1930s favored the growing American industrial base more than preserving nature. Environmental and employee issues took a back seat to industry. Laws relating to the protection of the environment were weak. In 1922, despite a ban in other countries, the United States refused to ban leaded paint. Because of its "anti-knock" properties, leaded gasoline became popular, even when the dangers were known. In 1924, the Oil Pollution Act was passed, prohibiting ships from dumping oil within three miles of the coast. But the act did nothing to address refineries

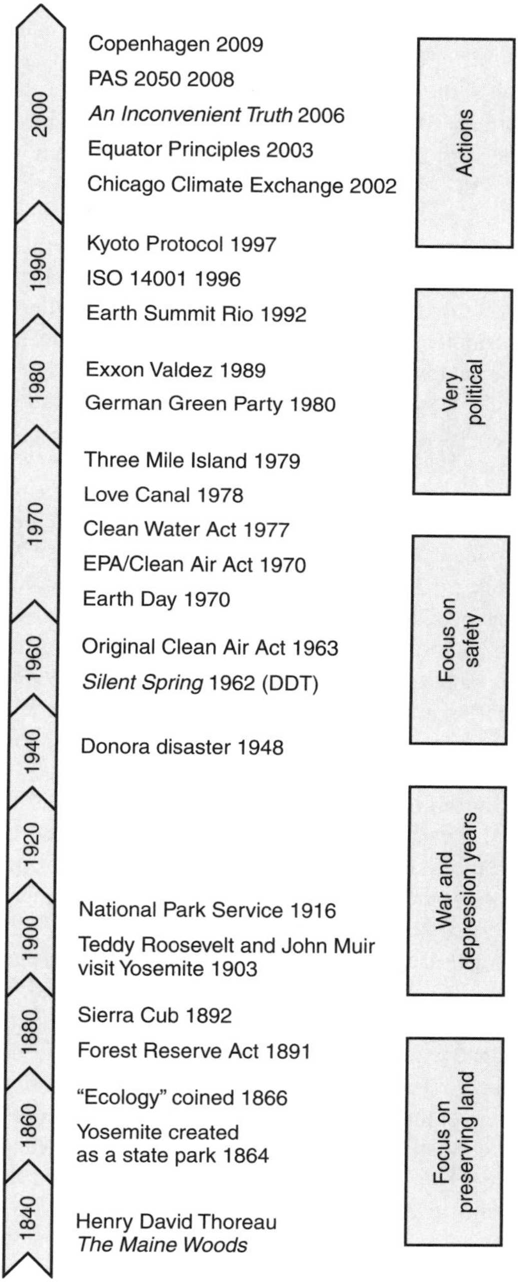
2000
1990
1980
1970
1960
1940
1920
1900
1880
1860
1840
Copenhagen 2009
PAS 2050 2008
An Inconvenient Truth 2006
Equator Principles 2003
Chicago Climate Exchange 2002
Kyoto Protocol 1997
ISO 14001 1996
Earth Summit Rio 1992
Exxon Valdez 1989
German Green Party 1980
Three Mile Island 1979
Love Canal 1978
Clean Water Act 1977
EPA/Clean Air Act 1970
Earth Day 1970
Original Clean Air Act 1963
Silent Spring 1962 (DDT)
Donora disaster 1948
National Park Service 1916
Teddy Roosevelt and John Muir visit Yosemite 1903
Sierra Cub 1892
Forest Reserve Act 1891
"Ecology" coined 1866
Yosemite created as a state park 1864
Henry David Thoreau The Maine Woods
Actions
Very political
Focus on safety
War and depression years
Focus on preserving land

Figure 1 Environmental time line.

dumping oil. Environmentalism was compared to nationalism and Nazism. Those comparisons still exist today among some people.

During the 1940s, the world focused on the war, and little attention was paid to the environment. After World War II, it was back to business making products for the world. American industry converted from war materials to consumer goods.

In 1948, the steel-manufacturing town of Donora, Pennsylvania, illustrated what can happen when industry and the environment cross paths in a really significant way. In an event that became known as the Donora Death Fog, a wall of smog settled over the town for four days and killed more than 20 people. Most attributed the catastrophe to fluorine gas from local industry that settled over the town during a temperature inversion.

In 1962, Rachel Carson published the book *Silent Spring*, bringing the impact of pesticides on the environment to the forefront.

The Clean Air Act, originally passed in 1963, was significantly strengthened by congress in 1970. Also in 1970, U.S. Senator Gaylord Nelson founded and Harvard student Denis Hayes coordinated the first Earth Day celebration. The purpose of Earth Day, according to Nelson, was "to shake up the political establishment and force the (environmental) issue onto the national agenda" (Earthday.net 2010).

In 1970, Congress formed the Environmental Protection Agency (EPA) with a mission that included "to protect human health and to safeguard the natural environment—air, water, and land—upon which life depends." For more than 30 years, the EPA has been working for "a cleaner, healthier environment for the American people" (epa.gov 2010).

The first EPA administrator was William D. Ruckelshaus, also known as "The Enforcer." He was known for going after polluters and stated in his keynote address to the International Clean Air Congress that the EPA had "no obligation to promote commerce or agriculture." He further stated that the EPA would enforce "reasonable standards of air quality." This clearly would not have made him a friend to industry. In 1971, Ruckelshaus rejected a schedule by Union Carbide to reduce sulfur oxide emissions from its Marietta plant. The company threatened to lay off 625 workers. A compromise was reached, the workers kept their jobs, and Union Carbide reduced emissions by 70 percent (epa.gov 2010).

At the same time, industry activists such as Ralph Nader were holding manufacturers accountable for their impact on both the environment and human safety. Early efforts by industry relating to safety and the environment were to prevent fines and bad publicity, not necessarily to protect the environment because it was the right thing to do.

With the passage of the Clean Air Act Extension in 1970 and the Clean Water Act in 1972, companies were required to follow regulations regarding emissions into air and water.

The argument by activists for greater environmental protection in the 1970s was strengthened following highly publicized environmental disasters caused by industry such as the Love Canal chemical dump, Union Carbide's Bhopal chemical release, and the *Exxon Valdez* oil spill.

The public demanded action to hold industry more accountable and keep them safe in the wake of these disasters, and the politicians attacked, attacked businesses, that is. Any mention of business and the environment started battles between the boardroom, the citizens, and Washington, D.C.

What about the loggers and the famous spotted owl? Today, the environmental argument centers on global warming and carbon emissions. The controversy is further complicated by arguments questioning whether global warming is really real and, if it is, whether or not it is really caused by humans.

The political nature of the global warming debate is evidenced by any mention of Al Gore's *An Inconvenient Truth* or discussions on the accuracy of climate data and an alleged cover-up dubbed "climategate" by British reporter James Delingpole.

As with the Clean Air Act and other past environmental legislation, political issues may very well generate laws that businesses must follow.

There is no question that there is great emphasis on the environment and becoming greener. Every day we see things that are already green and becoming greener. We are learning new phrases like *sustainable business, green manufacturing,* and *carbon credits.* Billboards tell us that congress will put us out of business if the climate bill passes. And all of this is taking place during the worst economy most of us can remember. As business owners and managers, we must figure out what green means to our businesses and take timely, cost-effective action to retain and win customers, or possibly to avoid expensive fines and/or taxes.

The time line in Figure 1 shows the early focus of environmentalists on preserving land, which led to action by the government to protect the land. The focus then shifted to worker and product safety, which led to legislation to provide safe products and safe workplaces. With the current focus on the environment and especially issues relating to greenhouse gases and global warming, one must consider the potential for new laws to be enacted that may impact businesses in these arenas.

SIGNIFICANT EVENTS IN CARBON REPORTING AND REDUCTION

The Rio Declaration on Environment and Development, sponsored by the United Nations Environment Programme known as Earth Summit in

June of 1992, built upon the commitment made at the Declaration of the United Nations Conference on the Human Environment in 1972. The original conference committed to a plan of sustainable development. The Rio Declaration then intended to stabilize greenhouse gas (GHG) emissions. A key part of this was to establish GHG inventories. This was called the United Nations Framework Convention on Climate Change (UNFCCC). Following ratification by the U.S. Senate, President George H. W. Bush signed the UNFCCC in October 1992. This treaty provided no carbon emission limits and was not legally binding. It did, however, provide for updates or protocols that would set legally binding limits on emissions. The principal update to this became known as the Kyoto Protocol.

The Kyoto Protocol, adopted in December 1997 and enforced in February 2005, did set limits on greenhouse gas emissions. Limits were established for 37 countries and the European community, with the intention of reducing emissions by five percent under 1990 levels. The protocol is legally binding, and 192 parties have signed it to date. The United States has not.

Kyoto set into place three market-based mechanisms that a company can use to adjust its official carbon emission calculation: carbon trading, clean development, and joint implementation. Carbon trading sets up a system by which parties that produce less than their allotment or emissions could trade or sell emissions to those who exceed their limit. The clean development mechanism allows parties to implement emission reduction or emission-free projects in developing countries to earn saleable emission credits. Joint implementation allows parties to implement emission reduction projects in other member countries to earn emission reduction units. For discussion on the industries spawned by this, see the section on offsetting.

Under the Kyoto Protocol, organizations must monitor emissions and track emissions trading. The Protocol set up a compliance mechanism that includes both a facilitative branch and an enforcement branch. The goal is to enforce the requirements of the Protocol and ensure integrity in carbon trading markets.

The Copenhagen Summit (UN Climate Change Conference) was held in December 2009. The goal of the conference was to write a treaty to address climate change issues.

By 2050 the UNFCCC would like to cut GHG concentrations to 50 percent under 2000 levels (Dell'Amore 2009). According to the UNFCCC, the conference has four main goals:

1. Define the amount by which developed countries will limit emissions

2. Determine how developing countries will limit emissions without limiting growth

3. Explore options to provide developing countries with financing for projects to reduce GHG emissions

4. Identify ways to treat participating countries as equal partners

The two major categories of GHG emissions are industrial activities (80%) and deforestation (20%).

Five major issues were explored by conference attendees, which included leaders from around the world (Garber 2010):

1. *Targets for cutting emissions.* According to the UNFCCC, the cut needs to be around 40%; the United States may agree to a 17% cut.

2. *Emissions from developed nations versus developing nations.* Most countries want the United States to slash emissions; however, the United States argues that developing nations such as China must also do their part in reducing emissions.

3. *Assistance to poor countries.* The World Bank estimates that poor countries will need $100 billion a year to respond to climate change.

4. *Carbon trading.* The general agreement is that the best way to manage carbon is to put a value on it and trade it on a global market; how to actually do that is very complicated.

5. *Pollution offsets.* If a country can not reduce its emissions, there may be options to offset those emissions by planting trees or reducing the number of trees cut down.

At the end of the conference, many were disappointed with the results. A legally binding agreement was not produced. However, some see the conference as a move in the right direction. It did produce the Copenhagen Accord, a nonbinding document that limits a global temperature increase to two degrees Celsius and provides aid to developing countries. Two degrees Celsius is considered the maximum allowable temperature increase to prevent interference with the planet's climate.

To business, the important thing to understand is that if a country commits to reducing emissions, all individual companies within that country may be required to demonstrate emission reduction and may be penalized for failure to do so.

HOW DOES GREEN RELATE TO YOUR BUSINESS?

Green is no longer progressive, but rather, expected.

—Johan de Nysschen, president, Audi of America

Let's suppose one of your major customers sent you a survey asking whether you measure your greenhouse gases and report those measurements. They also state that if you do not, you have six months to begin or you will be replaced by another supplier. Could you answer "yes" on the survey, or put practices in place to comply?

This scenario may not be as far-fetched as it sounds. In July 2009, Wal-Mart sent a Supplier Sustainability Survey to their suppliers with just those questions. They did not say the suppliers would be replaced if they didn't comply, but where do you think this will lead? Certainly, suppliers that do measure and report greenhouse gases will be more highly regarded than those that do not.

Sony, through its Green Partner Program, also requires suppliers to meet their environmental requirements and undergo audits for compliance.

As more large companies ask these questions of smaller companies with which they work, you can expect that environmental requirements will be prerequisites to doing business in the very near future.

Twenty-five or so years ago, there were very few manufacturing companies outside of defense contractors with documented and audited quality systems. In 1987, the International Organization for Standardization released the quality system standard ISO 9001. This standard was based on the British standard BS5750, and defined requirements for a quality management system. The large companies became compliant to this standard, and some demanded that suppliers do the same. Even if a registered ISO 9001 system is not required today, few customers will place an order with a company that has no documented quality system. I would expect this to be true in the future for an environmental management system that included carbon reporting and even sustainability issues.

To meet legal and customer requirements, business plans and procedures must be put into place and audited. These requirements relate to quality of products, employee safety, and environmental protection. Many times business is reactive to laws and regulations. In order to be more proactive, companies may adopt an environmental policy and commit to complying with environmental standards such as ISO 14001. An even more proactive approach would be to develop or adopt a system that seeks to reduce environmental impact through reducing and reporting waste and emissions.

Companies that became certified to the ISO 9001 quality standard often found that this standard alone was not sufficient to ensure a quality product and maintain satisfied customers. The same is becoming true with environmental practices. From the consumer's viewpoint, it will not be sufficient to meet an industry standard that they do not understand or of which they may not be aware. What will be required to win in the court of public opinion is a method to demonstrate environmental accountability and distinguish your goods and services from others.

Greenerchoices.org, a Web site launched in 2005 by the Consumers Union, which also publishes *Consumer Reports,* lists "Green Ratings" on products. Just as many consumers rely on performance and reliability data to make purchases, the trend seems also to include a green factor.

In a recent study commissioned by Green Seal and EnviroMedia Social Marketing, it is reported that four out of five people are still buying green products and services even if the products sometimes cost more (Green Seal 2009). On the other hand, the same study indicated that about one in three consumers indicated that they don't know whether green claims are true.

Claims about green products appear everywhere in marketing, from green cleaning products and shoes made from recycled materials to green-certified buildings. Consumers are recognizing the impact of products on the environment. As a business, you are being forced to understand the impact of the green revolution on your business. Initially, you must comply with the law and meet requirements imposed by your customers. But to maintain and grow your business, you must also differentiate your product, and this may very well mean addressing the green factor. A major question you need to ask yourself is, "Will green be part of my customers' purchase decisions?" If you are a supplier to Wal-Mart, Sony, or many other large firms, that question already may have been answered.

Green has expanded not only to address direct environmental impact, but also social issues such as fair trade, free range, and organics that relate to the conditions under which the product was produced. An early example of this is dolphin-safe tuna. In 1986, the International Marine Mammal Project encouraged a boycott of tuna due to the number of dolphins that were killed by tuna fishermen. Large tuna processors responded by purchasing tuna only from sources that met certain dolphin-safe standards. This led to the Dolphin-Safe Tuna Labeling Act in 1990.

In 2001, Sony had 1.3 million cables held in customs, preventing their distribution. The cables contained cadmium and were a part of a Christmas shipment. The cables had to be replaced at a cost to Sony of $130 million. Cadmium is a restricted substance addressed by the EU's Restriction of Hazardous Substances (RoHS) Directive. The policy Sony now imposes on its suppliers may be in place to prevent such an incident from happening again. But Sony also is taking a very proactive approach through the Green Partner program.

Will a consumer buy a pair of organic Levi jeans over the non-organic version? Only time will tell. But Levis has sold a lot of jeans based on the quality of their products, and the company may very well sell a lot more based on the green nature of their products.

Companies such as Ben & Jerry's have had success in the market with environmentally friendly and socially responsible products, sold at a premium price.

In today's marketplace, green goes beyond products. Internal processes are also becoming green. A search of the Internet will yield a green label for just about every function in an organization. There is green IT, green HR, green supply management, green shipping, green manufacturing, and the list goes on. So another question becomes, "Will the best employees favor working for green companies over the ones that are not as green?"

In the future, green may be the deciding factor for both customers and employees, a risk that should at least be addressed.

On the other hand, we are in business to satisfy our customers and make a profit. Auden Schendler (2010), in his book *Getting Green Done,* tells the story of wanting to retrofit the rooms of an upscale ski resort with compact fluorescent bulbs. The retrofit would have provided a 100 percent ROI in less than a year. The idea was rejected by the manager. The manager understood the impact on the environment, but he also understood that the retrofit would compromise his product, an upscale hotel room.

WHAT GREEN REALLY MEANS

From a business standpoint, forget the political battles over global warming and whether there is a relationship between greenhouse gas emissions and climate change. As a business, what matters is that there is great emphasis and importance being placed on going green and protecting the environment. While working toward green may not guarantee success, being anti-green may very well seal your demise as a business.

The irony of green is that everything we do has some sort of impact on the environment. Just talking about green has an impact. During the December 2009 Climate Change Conference in Copenhagen, the United Nations estimated that some 40,500 tons of carbon would be released in association with the event. That is the equivalent of about what 2000 Americans emit in a year. And American lifestyles emit about twice as much carbon as the global average.

If you drive your SUV to the store and bring home the groceries in a reusable bag, are you green? If you purchase an airline ticket and pay extra to "offset" the emissions, are you green? It's all relative. A dairy cow produces the equivalent of four tons of carbon per year, mostly from the methane in its waste. Just the act of breathing emits carbon. I realize these examples are a bit extreme, but it helps to think in those terms when trying to really understand something like green. So, can we ever truly be green? Well, that really depends on how we define green. Saying you have a green product is a lot like saying you have a quality product; both depend on your definition.

Two commonly accepted definitions of quality are "fit for purpose" and "meeting the requirements of the customer." Much like the definition of quality, the definition of green is difficult to pin down. But we really can't become green or offer green products if we don't know the definition of green. Some of the definitions put forth include:

- The immediate impact of our products and practices, and the residual impact of our products and practices (Michael Richmond, director of the Green Business League).

- A green building is an environmentally sustainable building designed, constructed, and operated to minimize the total environmental impacts (Build Green 2005).

- Having positive environmental attributes (BusinessDictionary.com).

- A business practice to conserve the natural environment and resources through processes that reduce or eliminate emissions and/or waste (California Employment Training Panel).

- Green computing is the environmentally responsible use of computers and related resources (techtarget.com).

- A green business is a business that operates in ways that solve, rather than cause both environmental and social problems (Green America).

- A green company uses practices that are viewed as sustainable and environmentally friendly (wisegeek.com).

There are several words that keep appearing in these and other definitions. These include *environment, responsible, social,* and *sustainable.* All of these are good words, but how do we measure green, and how do we know if our actions are making us more green or less green?

I would propose that the definition of green contain some measurable parameter and some requirement for continuous improvement. For example, one definition of a green company might be: "A socially responsible company that is committed to measuring, monitoring, and reducing its impact on the environment."

As far as measurement is concerned, measuring carbon emissions is rapidly becoming a popular tool for evaluating environmental impact. Measuring social responsibility may prove more difficult, but will also be discussed. In the *Wall Street Journal* article, "Six Products, Six Carbon Footprints," Jeffery Ball discusses the carbon footprint of products such as milk, shoes, and beer. The footprints ranged from seven pounds of carbon released for beer to 97,000 pounds for a car (Ball 2009). Ball also addresses the problem of how carbon is calculated and notes that there are many different ways to calculate a carbon footprint, making it almost impossible to compare different products.

These differences should not be viewed as a roadblock, but rather as an opportunity for companies to define their methods of carbon calculation, based on published standards. Just as there is no one way to measure quality, there is no one way to measure carbon emissions or environmental impact.

The common measures of green in use today are *carbon emissions, waste to landfills,* and *water usage.* An organization's green improvement efforts will most likely be related to one or more of these measurements.

GREENWASHING

No discussion of green would be complete without mentioning the recently coined term *greenwashing.* In a paper released in November of 2007, TerraChoice.com identified 1018 consumer products with 1753 environmental claims. Only one of the claims was determined not to be false or misleading. As a result TerraChoice developed the Seven Sins of Greenwashing (TerraChoice 2010).

These sins and the percentage of incidents found include:

1. *Sin of the hidden trade-off (57%).* Focusing on a narrow attribute such as recycled content without regard to other impacts.

2. *Sin of no proof (26%).* Promoting energy efficiency or recycled content without proof.

3. *Sin of vagueness (11%).* Statements such as chemical free or nontoxic.

4. *Sin of irrelevance (4%).* Promoting CFC free, since CFC has been banned for nearly 30 years.

5. *Sin of lesser of two evils (1%)*. Organic cigarettes.

6. *Sin of fibbing (less than 1%)*. Certified organic when no such certification exists.

7. *Sin of worshiping false labels.* A label or image gives the impression of a third-party endorsement when it does not exist.

Green Detectives

The Green Detectives, the founders of Tuerff-Davis Enviromedia, manage a Web page at www.greendetectives.net. Their goal is to promote authentic green marketing. They have an online forum that allows consumers to post and rate green ads and discuss their authenticity. The site provides current news regarding green advertising and a summary of green advertising ratings in its green scoring index.

Green Sheen

Green sheen, according to Wikipedia, describes an attempt to show that products or practices are beneficial to the environment. You see this in advertising that claims products are biodegradable or made using renewable energy sources.

When greening your products, processes, or services, be careful not to exaggerate your green claims to customers or employees. The commitment to green, like the commitment to quality, must be sincere. Making green claims and then not walking the talk will ensure failure of any efforts to become green. Just as making a commitment to quality and then knowingly shipping questionable products to make the numbers for the month will destroy a quality program, making green claims and not following through will be more harmful than doing nothing.

MEASURING, OFFSETTING, AND TRADING CARBON

Carbon emissions seem to be a popular way to measure our impact on the environment. No matter your position on the impact of carbon emission to the atmosphere, global warming, and all that, measuring carbon is a useful tool to convert energy consumption in various forms to a common measure. It provides a way to compare electricity usage to gasoline usage to coal usage, and to make any other comparisons we want.

Carbon emissions are typically reported in metric tons. A metric ton is 2204 U.S. pounds. Factors for carbon emitted per unit of most energy sources are readily available on the Internet and in texts relating to green. The EPA Web site (www.epa.gov) contains a wealth of information on the subject. Table 1 was compiled from information listed on www.carbonfund. org and referenced in many of the EPA's documents.

To calculate carbon emissions, it is just a matter of determining the amount associated with the activity and multiplying by the factor from the table. You will find there is some variation in the factors from source to source, but for practical purposes the differences are not significant. Actual calculation examples using Table 1 are demonstrated in a later chapter. Values listed in such tables are carbon equivalents and contain factors to include other gases. For example, when fuel is burned it releases both carbon dioxide and nitrous oxide.

Table 1   Carbon emission factors.

Activity	Carbon emissions (in lbs)	Per
Air cargo	1.7739	Ton-mile
Truck shipment	0.3725	Ton-mile
Train shipment	0.2306	Ton-mile
Sea freight	0.0887	Ton-mile
Electricity usage	1.297*	kWh
Natural gas	0.120593	Cubic foot
Heating oil	22.384	Gallon
Gasoline	19.4	Gallon
Car travel	0.7824*	Passenger mile
Short flight (500 miles)	0.5292	Passenger mile
Medium flight (1500 miles)	0.42	Passenger mile
Long flight (4000 miles)	0.3969	Passenger mile
Bus (city)	0.35	Passenger mile
Bus (long distance)	0.18	Passenger mile
Meals	2.756	Day
Hotel	65.11	Day

*National average

Many Web sites include carbon calculators where you simply enter the miles driven or electricity used and the carbon emissions are calculated for you.

THE GUILTY GASES

The term "greenhouse gas" is not a new one. This phrase was first introduced by Glenn Thomas Trewartha in his book, *An Introduction to Weather and Climate* in 1937. The gases were described as acting like an insulating blanket or a pane of glass in a greenhouse (Environmental History Timeline 2009).

Greenhouse gases are rated using a measure called the *global warming potential* (GWP). The GWP is a system that relates the potential of a gas to retain heat in the atmosphere. The rating also gives a 20-year, 100-year, and 500-year rating to account for how long the gas will remain in the atmosphere. Carbon has a GWP of 1, and the measurements given to all other gases are based on their relevance to carbon. Although carbon dioxide is the most common greenhouse gas, other gases are considered much more harmful. For example, sulfur hexafluoride has a 20-year GWP of 16,300 and a 100-year GWP of 23,900. This would indicate that sulfur hexafluoride retains much more heat than carbon and also remains in the atmosphere much longer.

Standard practice is to convert gases other than carbon dioxide to their carbon global warming potential equivalent for use in calculating emissions.

The gases at the center of the storm, those known as greenhouse gases (GHGs), include carbon dioxide, nitrous oxide, methane, sulfur hexafluoride, hydrofluorocarbons, perfluorochemicals, and fluorinated gases.

Carbon Dioxide (CO_2)

Carbon dioxide is emitted any time a fossil fuel, such as gasoline or coal, is consumed. It is by far the largest contributor to greenhouse gas emissions. Carbon dioxide also is emitted from natural sources such as decaying plants, volcanic eruptions, and even breathing.

Nitrous Oxide (N_2O)

Nitrous oxide is a by-product of combustion and has uses ranging from rocket fuel to medical applications. Nitrous oxide also is used as a propellant in whipped cream and to fill potato chip bags and cushion products.

Methane (CH$_4$)

Methane is introduced from both animal waste and decaying matter in landfills. In nature, it also can be emitted from wetlands, permafrost, and wildfires.

Sulfur Hexafluoride (SF$_6$)

Sulfur hexafluoride has electronic applications in circuit breakers and as an insulator gas. SF$_6$ also has several medical applications, including ultrasound and eye surgery.

Hydrofluorocarbons (HFCs)

Hydrofluorocarbons replaced banned ozone-depleting chlorofluorocarbons and are used as a refrigerant and also as a propellant in aerosol cans.

Perfluorochemicals (PFCs)

Perfluorochemicals are used as fire-fighting foam, and also found in non-stick coatings and stain-resistant materials. They are marketed with trade names such as Teflon, Stainmaster, Scotchgard, and Gore-Tex.

Fluorinated Gases

- *Nitrogen trifluoride* is used for silicon wafer manufacturing and in liquid crystal displays (LCD).
- *Hydrofluorinated ethers (HFEs)* are used in solvents with medical and industrial applications.

According to the United Nations Framework Convention on Climate Change, global warming potentials are as shown in Table 2.

Offsetting

There are several companies offering ways to "offset" your carbon production by purchasing carbon credits. The way this works is that you calculate your carbon emissions using the provided calculator for your home or business. Once the total carbon emissions are known, you can offset that carbon by paying the going rate per ton of carbon. As of this writing, the cost to offset varied from about $2.00 to $25.00 per ton, depending on the organization. The money received from offsetting is then used for various projects

Table 2 Global warming potentials.

Gas	Life (Years)	20-year GWP	100-year GWP	500-year GWP
Carbon	Various	1	1	1
Methane	12	56	21	6.5
Nitrous oxide	120	280	310	170
Sulfur Hexafluoride	3200	16,300	23,900	34,900
Hydrofluorocarbons	1.5–265	490–9100	140–11,700	42–9800
Perfluorochemicals	3200–10,000	4400–6000	6500–9200	10,000–14,000

designed to reduce carbon emissions in the future. These include investments in renewable energy, energy efficiency, and reforestation. Many of the organizations that offer this service claim to have third-party verification of the projects.

There is controversy that surrounds the practice of offsetting. What is the money really going for? If trees are planted, are they maintained so they actually reach maturity? The controversy is not only over where the money goes, but whether the offset actually does any good. The paper "The Carbon Neutral Myth" by Kevin Smith compares offsetting to paying for your sins instead of repenting. In other words, a Hollywood star that lives a lavish, carbon-intensive life style can buy offsets instead of actually reducing their carbon emissions. Using this method, you can become carbon neutral by just paying for your carbon emissions and without actually doing anything (Smith 2007).

The concept of carbon offsetting is closely linked with carbon trading, where a carbon credit is created by an activity that prevents the release of carbon emissions, has some value, and can then be sold. For example, the organization Climate Care has a project in India where diesel irrigation pumps are replaced with manually operated treadle pumps. According to Climate Care, by replacing the diesel engines, emissions have been reduced 177,000 tons over four years (ClimateCare 2009).

There is a commodity-type market developing around this concept, where people seek out projects to reduce carbon, claim those credits, and then sell the credits to consumers or industries that emit carbon. According to the show *Carbon Hunters: Making Money out of Thin Air* on CNBC, which aired April 25, 2010, carbon offset trading is emerging as one of the century's biggest businesses. People called carbon hunters are searching for and selling the resulting carbon credits for capturing carbon (CNBC 2010).

Carbon Trading

The Chicago Climate Exchange (CCX), at the time of this writing, is the only North American cap and trade system for greenhouse gases. The CCX membership list includes organizations from just about every industry and service. Members enter into a legally binding but voluntary contract to meet carbon reduction requirements. Companies that reduce carbon emissions to below their target can bank or sell "contracts" (100 metric tons of CO_2 equivalents) to those who exceed emissions.

Following are the goals and benefits of joining CCX as listed on their Web page (Chicago Climate Exchange 2010):

Goals (Chicago Climate Exchange)

1. To facilitate the transaction of GHG allowance trading with price transparency, design excellence, and environmental integrity

2. To build the skills and institutions needed to cost-effectively manage GHGs

3. To facilitate capacity-building in both public and private sectors to facilitate GHG mitigation

4. To strengthen the intellectual framework required for cost-effective and valid GHG reduction

5. To help inform the public debate on managing the risk of global climate change

Benefits

1. Be prepared: mitigate financial, operational, and reputational risks

2. Reduce emissions using the highest compliance standards with third-party verification

3. Prove concrete action on climate change to shareholders, rating agencies, customers, and citizens

4. Establish a cost-effective, turnkey emissions management system

5. Drive policy developments based on practical, hands-on experience

6. Gain leadership recognition for taking early, credible, and binding action to address climate change

7. Establish early track record in reductions and experience with growing carbon and GHG market

In the event that a cap and trade–type system becomes law, such an exchange will be the method by which excess carbon units could be sold to those companies that do not meet their reduction targets.

CARBON REPORTING ORGANIZATIONS

Several organizations have developed standards and databases for carbon reporting. Most reporting methods are based on the Greenhouse Gas Protocol discussed below (GHG Protocol Initiative 2009). The goal of these organizations is to provide voluntary, accurate, and verifiable data on member companies. Most of the organizations provide data for benchmarking free of charge.

The Climate Registry

The Climate Registry was founded in 2008 and defined a reporting protocol based on the GHG Protocol for use by North American companies. The Climate Registry utilizes a database, the Climate Registry Information System (CRIS), to maintain reported data. It also provides a protocol for verification of climate data.

The Climate Registry defines various options for reporting based on how the company is controlled and where it is located. It also has options for both direct and indirect emission reporting. The reporting standard has a provision for facility-level reporting that includes emissions from transportation and requires establishment of a base year to benchmark future emissions. The base year can be adjusted to consider changes in the business.

The Climate Registry developed a protocol for voluntary reporting of greenhouse gas emissions. It lists the benefits of reporting as risk management, competitive advantage, readiness for emissions trading, readiness for a carbon-constrained future, recognition as an environmental leader, and participation in key policy discussions (Climate Registry 2008).

The protocol defines what is to be reported and how to report it, and provides a database to store the information. The Climate Registry is based on the GHG Protocol reporting standard and is an effort to unify various national, state, and regional reporting bodies.

The General Reporting Protocol (GRP) is available online from www.climateregistry.org/tools/protocols/general-reporting-protocol.html. The protocol contains definitions and many useful flowcharts for determining what and how to report. ISO 14064 is based on this protocol.

GHG Protocol

According to its Web site, www.ghgprotocol.org, the GHG Protocol is the most widely used reporting protocol. The Climate Registry model is based on the GHG Protocol. The GHG Protocol is an international body, and its standard, *The Greenhouse Gas Protocol: A Corporate Accounting and Reporting Standard,* was published in 2001. The GHG Protocol has developed many guidance documents and worksheet-based reporting tools. The GHG Protocol partnered with the World Resources Institute and the World Business Council for Sustainable Development, who are working toward "credible and effective programs for tackling climate change" (GHG Protocol Initiative 2009).

The Carbon Trust Standard

The Carbon Trust is an independent company set up by the UK government to work with organizations to develop low-carbon technologies that will reduce carbon emissions (Carbon Trust 2009).

The Carbon Trust certifies UK companies to the standard. Requirements for certification dictate that an organization measure its carbon footprint accurately, achieve a reduction in that footprint, and use reduction methods that meet the standard. The Trust provides both a carbon footprint calculator and an assessment guide. The assessment process is similar to becoming ISO 9001 or ISO 14001 certified. Reporting is in accordance with the GHG Protocol guidelines.

Carbon Disclosure Project

The Carbon Disclosure Project (CDP) was launched in 2000 with the goal of collecting and distributing information that motivates corporations and governments to take action to prevent climate change.

According to its Web page, some 2500 organizations in 60 countries participate. Membership is divided into three categories: investor, supply chain, and public procurement. The data maintained includes general company information, physical and financial, regulatory risks and opportunities, actual carbon emissions, and responsibilities for managing emissions. Data are reported in accordance with GHG Protocol and ISO 14064 (Carbon Disclosure Project 2009).

The CDP is an outlet for companies to disclose carbon emissions and carbon reduction strategies. The CDP also provides information valuable to companies benchmarking performance, as the reports are readily available online.

Climate Leaders

Climate Leaders is an EPA industry–government partnership to develop climate change strategies (EPA Climate Leaders 2010). The EPA launched Climate Leaders in 2002 with 11 initial partners.

Partners commit to reporting GHG emissions based on a quality management system, setting aggressive goals, and reducing and reporting emissions. As of this writing, more than 250 companies were listed as participants. Partners are listed in one of three categories: *goal achievers, goal setters,* and *goals under development.*

Members range from large corporations to small businesses, and they receive free technical assistance in developing a GHG inventory, management plan, and reduction goal.

Global Reporting Initiative

The Global Reporting Initiative (GRI) is a network-based sustainability reporting framework that maintains goals and performance data in the areas of economic, social, and environmental performance (Global Reporting Initiative 2010).

Founded in 1997, the organization maintains thousands of reports in its database. These reports are available online.

See Table 3 for a summary of carbon reporting organizations.

Table 3 Reporting standards summary.

Name	Standard	Area served	Data collection	Purpose	Web page
GHG Protocol	Yes	International	Yes	Most widely used method	www.ghgprotocol.org
The Climate Registry		North America	Climate Information Registry System (CRIS)	Associated with GHG Protocol	www.theclimateregistry.org
Carbon Trust standard	Yes	UK	No	Support and certification body	www.carbontrust.com
Carbon Disclosure Project	Use GHG Protocol	International	Yes—Results available online	Data collection and distribution	www.cdproject.net
Climate Leaders	Climate Registry format	United States	Yes	Members receive free technical assistance	www.epa.gov/stateply
Global Reporting Initiative	Reporting standard	International	Yes	Framework for reporting social and environmental performance	www.globalreporting.org

Section 2

Standards, Certifications, and References

With all the talk about the impact a carbon trading program or a carbon cap and trade scheme may bring, it is important to remember that the United States has such a program already in place. It is not a cap on carbon, but a cap on sulfur dioxide. The program is known as the Acid Rain Program. According to the EPA, this program has been successful in reducing sulfur dioxide emissions by 50 percent, while power consumption increased by 50 percent, since 1980. One would have to expect that a similar program will be implemented for carbon.

STANDARDS AND DIRECTIVES

For now, there are several standards, directives, and pieces of legislation worth mentioning that directly relate to what we are calling green. This section is by no means meant to be a complete list or to address every detail of the documents referenced. The purpose of this section is to introduce the reader to some typical standards and attempts that have been made to standardize what green means.

After the Uruguay General Agreement on Tariffs and Trade (GATT) and the Rio Summit in 1992, the International Organization for Standardization (ISO) developed a standard that specifies "requirements for an environmental management system to enable an organization to formulate a policy and objectives, taking into account legislative requirements and information about significant environmental impacts." This standard, ISO 14001, became the minimum requirement for a company's environmental system, much as ISO 9001 that preceded it impacted a company's quality management system.

ISO 14001 was first released by the International Organization for Standardization as a management tool to control an organization's impact on the environment. The standard requires organizations to "establish, document, implement, maintain and continuously improve an environmental management system" (ISO 2004). Compliance to the standard is not a legal requirement, but may be required by customers. The standard generally follows the ISO 9001 quality management system standard, which requires that organizations meet certain requirements in regard to how they manage quality.

The intent of the standard is to provide a framework around which an organization can build an effective system to determine, monitor, and reduce its environmental impact. If an organization wants to be certified to the standard, it requires a third-party audit by an accredited firm.

Since the introduction of ISO 14001, there have been many standards developed and released to address environmental, green, and sustainability issues. The list below is not all-inclusive, but includes current standards that are seen as significant in developing a suitable system for environmental management and carbon reporting.

In late 2010, another standard, ISO 26000, *Guidance on social responsibility*, is scheduled to be released. It will address a wide range of topics, from protecting human rights to protecting the environment. Measuring greenhouse gases and environmental management will be subset requirements of this standard.

Two other directives from the European Union (EU) have significant impact on business. The directive Restriction of Hazardous Substances (RoHS) and the directive Waste from Electrical and Electronic Equipment (WEEE) mandates the recovery and recycling of electronic products.

RoHS

The Restriction of Hazardous Substances, (RoHS—commonly pronounced "row-hoss" or "ross"), is a European Union (EU) directive requiring that certain substances be eliminated from products sold in the EU. Banned substances include lead, mercury, cadmium, hexavalent chromium, polybrominated biphenyls (PBB), and polybrominated diphenyl ethers (PBDE). The requirement went into effect in July 2006. There were several exemptions allowed. As of this writing, the list includes 38 exemptions, and this list continues to be updated. The exemptions tend to be very specific and apply where suitable replacement materials or processes can not be found, for example, using lead as an alloying element in steel (*Official Journal of the European Union* 2003a).

The directive is also referred to as the "lead-free" directive due to its impact on the electronics industry, which used solder that contained lead.

WEEE

The purpose of the Waste Electrical and Electronic Equipment (WEEE) directive is to prevent waste electrical and electronic equipment, and to encourage reuse, recycling, and recovery of such equipment in order to reduce the environmental impact of these products.

The directive encourages manufacturers to build products designed to facilitate disassembly and recovery, and requires organizations to set up systems to recover products at the end of their useful life cycles. The directive applies to products from small household appliances to mainframe computers. To indicate that these products can be recycled, they are identified with a "crossed out wheelie bin," or trash can (*Official Journal of the European Union* 2003b).

Unlike ISO 14001 and the other ISO standards discussed here where compliance is voluntary, compliance with RoHS and WEEE is mandatory for products going to the EU.

PAS 2050

Developed by the British Standards Institution (BSI), the Publicly Available Specification (PAS) PAS 2050 is a standard that defines a method of assessing the life cycle greenhouse gas emissions of goods and services (British Standards Insitution 2009).

PAS 2050 applies to all goods and services, considers the life cycle from supply to disposal, and addresses the greenhouse gases covered by the Kyoto Protocol. Along with the standard, there is a guide with step-by-step examples for calculating GHG emissions.

ISO 14064

This standard, published by the International Organization for Standardization and approved in 2006, is based on the GHG Protocol reporting standard and is recognized as an international standard. It is divided into three sections:

1. A specification with guidance at the organizational level for quantification, monitoring, and reporting of greenhouse gas emission and removals

2. A specification with guidance at the project level for quantification, monitoring, and reporting of greenhouse gas emission reductions or removal enhancements

3. A specification with guidance for the validation and verification and certification of greenhouse gas assertions

This standard allows companies to become certified in the same manner in which they became certified to the ISO 9001 and ISO 14001 standards.

Areas addressed by the ISO 14064 standard include organizational boundaries and reporting based on either control or equity, GHG inventories and types of greenhouse gases, establishment of a base year for reporting, GHG inventory quality management, and GHG reporting requirements.

ISO 26000

Projected to be released late in 2010, ISO 26000 addresses social requirements of business. This will be a guidance document, not meant as audit requirements. The document makes the link between social responsibility and sustainability. This is a far-reaching document, addressing such topics as human rights, labor practices, health and safety, human development, corruption, fair competition, and a host of other social issues. Environmental management is one element of this document. The environmental section of ISO 26000 defines four environmental issues:

1. *Pollution prevention.* This section requires an organization to improve its environmental performance by preventing pollution to air, water, land, and soil by reducing waste and hazardous substances.

2. *Sustainable resource use.* This section requires organizations to take action to ensure that resources are available in the future by implementing energy-efficient programs, conserving water, and efficiently using materials.

3. *Climate change mitigation and adaptation.* This section requires organizations to measure and minimize emissions, as well as plan for future impacts of climate change.

4. *Environmental protection and restoration.* This section requires the organization to identify impacts on the ecosystem and take actions to reduce the impact on, protect, preserve, and restore the environment, including natural habitat and endangered species.

ISO 26000 could very well become the standard for customer sustainability audits. As mentioned earlier, Wal-Mart and other customers are doing sustainability surveys.

As of today, there are various standards and guidelines for sustainability, carbon reporting, and environmental management that are emerging.

Unless a customer has already decided what method or standard to use, the choice may be yours. Even if you choose not to follow a standard and develop a protocol based on your individual company's needs, it will demonstrate your company's commitment to the environment and sustainability issues. Just as many companies have their own unique quality systems, many will develop their own environmental management systems. As long as the factors and methods used clearly demonstrate compliance, this will be a very acceptable start to becoming green.

ISO 14020

The ISO 14020 series of standards, ISO 14024, type I for eco-labeling programs, type II self-declared environmental claims, and type III environmental product declarations, are meant to provide a standard method to convey environmental claims to the market (Committee on Trade and Investment 2003).

Examples of type I labeling are the eco-mark in Japan and the Environmental Choice in Canada. The intent is to show that products with this label are environmentally preferable to those without it.

Type II labels, self-declaration claims, are designed to market products to environmentally conscious customers.

Type III labels are similar to type II labels; however, the target is industrial customers as opposed to retail customers.

ISO 14040

The ISO 14040 series of standards provides a method for evaluating environmental aspects and impacts of a product from raw material acquisition to production and end of life.

ISO 14062

ISO 14062 addresses integrating environmental aspects into product design and development.

See Table 4 for a summary of key standards. The table includes a column for the process stage to which the standard applies.

Clean Air Act

In 1970, Congress revised and strengthened the original Clean Air Act passed in 1963. The EPA was formed and given the role of enforcing this act. Congress expanded the Clean Air Act again in 1990. The Act set limits

Table 4 Standards summary.

Standard	Title	Stage of process
ISO 14064-1	*Greenhouse Gases—Part 1: Specification with guidance at the organization level for quantification and reporting of greenhouse gas emissions and removals*	Planning/management
ISO 14064-2	*Greenhouse gases—Part 2: Specification with guidance at the project level for quantification, monitoring and reporting of greenhouse gas emission reductions or removal enhancements*	Planning/management
ISO 14064-3	*Greenhouse gases—Part 3: Specification with guidance for the validation and verification of greenhouse gas assertions*	Auditing
ISO 14001	*Environmental management system requirements— Requirements with guidance for use*	Planning/management
ISO 14020	*Environmental labels and declarations—General principles*	Marketing
ISO 14040	*Environmental Management— Life cycle assessment— Principles and framework*	Marketing
ISO 14041	*Environmental management— Life cycle assessment— Examples of application of ISO 14041 to goal and scope definition and inventory analysis*	Design
ISO 14042	*Environmental management— Life cycle impact assessment— Examples of application of ISO 14042*	Design
ISO 14043	*Life cycle assessment—Life cycle interpretation*	Design

Continued

Table 4   *Continued.*

Standard	Title	Stage of process
ISO 14047	*Environmental management— Life cycle impact assessment— Examples of application of ISO 14042*	Design
ISO 14062	*Environmental management— Integrating environmental aspects into product design and development*	Design
ISO 14048	*Environmental management— Life cycle assessment—Data documentation format*	Design
ISO 14050	*Environmental management— vocabulary*	All
ISO 14049	*Environmental management— Life cycle assessment— Examples of application of ISO 14041 to goal and scope definition and inventory analysis*	Design
ISO 14065	*Greenhouse gases— Requirements for greenhouse gas validation and verification bodies for use in accreditation or other forms of recognition*	Design verification/ validation
ISO 26000	*Guidance on social responsibility*	Outlines all aspects of a socially responsible organization
ISO 9001	*Quality management systems— Requirements*	Quality systems mangement
ISO 9004	*Managing for the sustained success of an organization—A quality management approach*	Planning
PAS 2050	*Assessing the life cycle greenhouse gas emissions of goods and services*	Product and service–based GHG calculation methodology
ISO 14004	*Environmental management systems—General guidelines on principles, systems and support techniques*	Planning/management

Continued

Table 4 *Continued.*

Standard	Title	Stage of process
ISO 14061	*Information to assist forestry organizations in the use of ISO 14001 and ISO 14004*	Planning/management
ISO 14015	*Environmental management— Environmental assessment of sites and organizations (EASO)*	Auditing
ISO 19011	*Guidelines for quality and/or environmental management systems auditing*	Auditing
ISO 14031	*Environmental management— Environmental performance evaluation—guidelines*	Planning/management
ISO Guide 64	*Guide for addressing environmental issues in product standards*	Design
ISO 14062	*Environmental management— Integrating environmental aspects into product design and development*	Design
ISO 14021	*Environmental labels and declarations—Self-declared environmental labels*	Marketing
ISO 14024	*Environmental labels and declarations—Type I environmental labeling*	Marketing
ISO 14025	*Environmental labels and declarations—Type III environmental labeling*	Marketing

on the amount of pollutant emissions allowed from various sources. The EPA states, "since 1970, the six commonly found air pollutants have decreased by more than 50 percent, while the GDP has tripled and energy consumption has increased by 50 percent."

Clean Water Act

The Clean Water Act, passed in 1972, was designed to reduce direct discharge into waterways and manage polluted runoff. The act uses both regulatory and nonregulatory methods to accomplish the goal.

Current EPA Thinking

The EPA will be key to determining what U.S. businesses will be required to do concerning greenhouse gas issues. In December 2009, an action was signed proclaiming that the six greenhouse gases constitute a threat to public health and welfare and that emissions contribute to the climate change problem. A valuable source of information can be found on the EPA's climate change Web site at www.epa.gov/climatechange. This site contains current news and links to EPA requirements and programs concerning GHG emissions and reporting.

SETTING THE STANDARD: GREEN LABELS, SEALS, AND CERTIFICATION

Several organizations have developed certifications for products to demonstrate compliance to a standard that relates to being environmentally friendly or socially responsible. These certifications are product-specific and vary from industry to industry. These ratings also may include a measure of energy efficiency.

The standards reflect different industries' attempts to define what green means for that industry.

Fair Trade Certification

Fair trade certification "empowers farmers and farm workers to lift themselves out of poverty by investing in their farms and communities, protecting the environment, and developing the business skills necessary to compete in the global marketplace." (TransFair USA 2010.)

In addition to dealing with price, fair trade addresses labor conditions, direct trade issues, community development, and environmental sustainability of agricultural products. Fair trade certification is available in the United States for several grown imported products, including coffee, chocolate, and sugar.

Currently TransFair USA, the third-party certifier of fair trade products, allows over 600 U.S. companies to display the fair trade certified label on their products.

LEED

Leadership in Energy and Environmental Design (LEED) is a recognized green building certification that addresses several factors of construction and operation. LEED measures key areas of performance, including site sustainability, water and energy efficiency, materials usage, and indoor environmental quality. The green building certificate ensures, through third-party verification, that a building is constructed to meet the defined requirements. LEED uses a rating system with 110 possible points and rates a building as certified with 40–49 points, silver certified with 50–59 points, gold certified with 60–79 points, or platinum certified with 80+ points. Ratings are conducted in the following categories (U.S. Green Building Council 2010):

1. Sustainable sites

2. Water efficiency

3. Energy and atmosphere

4. Materials and resources

5. Indoor environmental quality

6. Bonus point categories

7. Innovation in design

8. Regional priority

Green Seal

The Green Seal certification mark on a product indicates that the product has been scientifically evaluated and meets requirements aimed at reducing its impact on the environment. There are Green Seal categories for cleaners, paper, paint, windows/doors, and hotels.

Founded in 1989, Green Seal issued its first environmental standards in 1991 and completed product certifications in 1992. At the present time, Green Seal has more than 40 product-specific standards.

To have a product certified, a request is made to Green Seal, this request is reviewed, and the proper audit is conducted. If the audit is successful and a product meets the requirements, the manufacturer is permitted to use the Green Seal on its product.

Green Seal issues "Green Reports" on many products, from office supplies to lawn care equipment. These reports describe the materials the products are made of, including recycled content, and make recommendations on which types of products to buy in order to be more environmentally friendly.

Since 1995, Green Seal has worked with the lodging and restaurant industry to promote environmentally friendly practices. Green Seal offers different certification levels based on criteria relating to waste, water management, and purchasing practices.

For example, gold-level certification requires that 80 percent of purchases be organic or environmentally preferable, there is demonstration of a 25 percent reduction in red meat sales, 15 percent improvement in energy conservation, diversion of 90 percent of waste from landfills, double-sided printing with vegetable ink, 30 percent of business miles driven using hybrid or alternative fuel vehicles, and the development of a publicly available annual report on environmental and social responsibility (Green Seal 2010).

Energy Star

Energy Star is a joint program with the United States EPA that provides energy consumption ratings on thousands of electrical products. Product ratings, along with many useful tools to evaluate and improve energy efficiency, can be found on the Web page www.energystar.gov.

Greenguard

Greenguard is a nonprofit organization responsible for certifying products and buildings that meet certain air quality requirements. Products ranging from flooring to paint are tested and certified to be low emitting. A current list of certified products is maintained on their Web page www.greenguard.org.

Scientific Certification Systems

Scientific Certification Systems is an independent certification body that manages standards and certification programs relating to environmental, social accountability, and product performance. Industries served include agricultural, food, forestry, fisheries, plants, retail, and buildings.

The Alliance for Telecommunications Industry Solutions (ATIS)

ATIS is an industry organization comprising representatives from over 250 communications companies. ATIS develops standards for information technology (IT) and communications products. Recently, ATIS published several standards that address the energy efficiency of network and telecommunications equipment. The organization also has developed a telecommunications energy efficiency ratio (TEER) rating that defines a method for vendors and third parties to rate products (ATIS 2010).

Forest Stewardship Council

The Forest Stewardship Council certifies that wood comes from a forest managed in an environmentally responsible, socially beneficial, and economically viable way. The council has developed a set of principles and criteria by which forests should be managed. The criteria require that organizations comply with all laws, protect the rights of indigenous populations and species, and manage impacts, among other activities.

Green Vehicle Rating

Another example of a green rating is the EPA Green Vehicle rating. This rating system gives vehicles an air pollution score and a greenhouse gas score. The air pollution score is based on EPA emission standards, and the greenhouse gas score is based on emissions that result from operating the vehicle.

Greener Choices

Greenerchoices.org, which is associated with *Consumer Reports,* has green ratings for products in categories such as cars, electronics, appliances, and home and garden products. The Web site also tests and verifies product environmental and energy consumption claims. In recent reports, Greener Choices found energy consumption of several refrigerators to be as much as 50 percent higher than the labels claimed.

With these programs and many others in place, and more on the horizon, the question for business is not whether a rating or compliance to a green standard will impact sales, but how much the impact will be.

See Table 5 for a list of various certifications.

Table 5 Green certifications.

Name	Products addressed	Type of service	Web site
Fair trade certification	Agricultural products	Product certification	transfairusa.org
LEED	Buildings	Building certification	usgbc.org
Green Seal	Many products including services	Product certification	greenseal.org
Energy Star	Electrical products and building	Ratings based on energy usage	energystar.gov
Greenguard	Construction, building, and school air quality	Certification	greenguard.org
Scientific Certification Systems	Many products	Certification	scscertified.com
Forest Stewardship Council	Forest products	Certification	fscus.org
ATIS	IT and telecom products	Standard	ATIS.org

Section 3

Implementing and Managing Green

THE RELATIONSHIP BETWEEN GREEN AND QUALITY

Green is the new *quality*. I say this because many questions that relate to "green" today are like the questions that surrounded "quality" several years ago and persist today. Although we all know what quality is when we see it, it would be difficult to get a consistent definition of quality if several people were asked.

I discovered that the effort to become a green company was very similar, in fact almost identical, to efforts to build a quality company.

My training and experience employing the tools of quality and process improvement were useful for defining and measuring the sometimes abstract concept of green. As a quality professional, you fundamentally know that in order to improve a product or process you need to understand it and know how to measure it. You also know that to control it, an organization must rely on solid processes that are implemented and audited on a regular basis.

Like quality, green has no universal definition, can be difficult to measure, and will always leave room for improvement. Just as a quality system that complies with an ISO standard does not guarantee a quality product or quality process, compliance to a particular environmental standard will not guarantee an environmentally friendly company.

Environmental requirements will vary greatly by industry and organization; furthermore, the ISO series of standards provides a general reference intended to be general enough for all organizations. The standards are popular in manufacturing-type organizations but have not been widely adopted by many other types of organizations. Most likely your local supermarket will never be compliant to either ISO 9001 or ISO 14001, but you still expect a quality product from a company that is not harming the environment. A hospital or financial firm may never adopt an ISO standard but can certainly manage and reduce their environmental impacts.

The ISO standards provide a valuable reference and are a good starting point, but like quality, the concept of being green and protecting the environment must be much more than compliance to a standard.

Just as a company can never achieve perfect quality, it also can never be perfectly green. As stated earlier, industry converts resources into something it can sell, be it a product or service.

The parallels between the quest for green and the quest for quality are endless. The organization has the tools, knowledge, and experience to understand and implement procedures to help a company define, implement, and manage a process that helps the company become environmentally friendly, while reducing costs.

Some of the parallels between green and quality include:

1. No universal definition

2. Difficult to measure

3. Not directly listed in financials, unless there is a problem

4. No one group in the organization has complete responsibility

5. Good for marketing, but may be considered a trade-off in financials or operations

6. Not completely achievable (nothing is perfect and nothing is completely green)

7. Based on a philosophy that may have different meaning to different people

8. Is a process that must be continuously managed

9. Focus can easily be lost in the short term to items considered a higher priority, for example, profitability or making shipments

10. Can be seen as expensive, with little short-term gain

11. Environmental management and carbon reporting standards exist that are similar to ISO 9001

12. Customers may demand it with very little definition of exactly what they want

13. Requirements and measurements are unique to each industry

GREEN IS FREE

In 1979, Philip Crosby published his landmark book on quality, *Quality Is Free*. This was released in a time when it was thought that increasing the quality of a product to be more competitive would increase its cost. Crosby indicated just the opposite is true. Now, in a time when companies are balancing the cost of protecting the environment, staying in business, meeting pending legislation, and becoming green, maybe we should dust off that old copy of Crosby's book.

Instead of looking at what makes a product green, let's look at what the opposite of green is. If a product or service is not green, then it must contain waste that is harmful to the environment. This waste could be in the form of excess emissions from inefficient transportation or heating/cooling of a building. It could be excess material going to the landfill. It could be the inefficient use of any of the resources needed to run the business. Reduction of any of the above forms of waste would have a direct and measurable impact on a company's bottom line by saving cash. Less direct and maybe less measurable is the ability to sell our products in the market by demonstrating that the product is green or was produced using an efficient green process, not to mention the market opportunities that new green products and technologies would offer.

Looking at the state of green today, we see a situation that reminds me of the criticism of the famous fourteen points of quality expert Dr. W. Edwards Deming. Many said that he put forth goals without providing the tools. He has been quoted as responding, "You are the manager, you figure it out." Dr. Deming's point was that management must take responsibility, define the plan of action, and lead the effort in executing that plan. Today, the case for green is no different. Management must step up and define what green means to the company, then lead the organization in meeting that definition.

Typically, when a company (management) claims to be green, that claim can mean just about anything, from sustainability, to environmentally friendly, to all sorts of things that just are not measurable. In my experience as a Six Sigma instructor, I have lost track of the number of times I have told students that if they can not measure their output, they do not have a project.

> *Measure what is measurable, and make measurable what is not so.*
>
> —Galileo

The same is true with becoming green or sustainable. If there is no way to measure it, then what does it really mean?

Our experience in process improvement tells us that in order to get management involved, we need to demonstrate the impact on the bottom line. In other words, we need to demonstrate how going green is going to save money and/or increase sales and profitability. As with any improvement project, the item we are trying to improve needs to be clearly stated in measurable terms. The things that come to mind as measurable and impactful when it comes to green are waste and carbon emissions.

In any business, waste in all of its forms is always a good thing to reduce. The interesting thing here is that carbon emissions and waste are not independent. Waste from consuming excess fuel turns into excess carbon emissions; waste from material going into the landfill consumes excess resources and ends up as carbon emissions. Waste due to the lack of recycling material and using additional resources to reproduce material that could have been recycled also increases carbon emissions.

For our primary green metric, we could just measure carbon emissions. Based on the laws being discussed at the time of this writing, carbon emissions may soon have to be measured for legal compliance anyway.

Another metric could be waste. For example, we could measure the amount of material disposed of that ends up in the landfill, or the amount of water used during production. As with any metric, it is important to have a metric that is understandable and actionable. If, for example, we declare that we are going to be a green company and do not define what green means, we can't expect much to happen. But if we say we are going to be a green company, and that means reducing carbon emissions or waste by 10 percent each year—and further that we are going to do that by reducing fuel, electric, and water usage—we now have a measureable and understandable metric that can be acted on.

Other metrics to consider would be the amount of material being recycled, reductions in shipping weights or distances, and even reductions in employee or business travel. We will see in later sections that any reduction in transportation can have a significant impact on carbon emissions.

I would propose that we use some combination of waste and carbon emissions as measurement metrics. Any time a fuel is consumed, it is easy to directly calculate the amount of carbon emitted. If material is recycled, the amount recycled may be more meaningful than reporting the carbon not emitted from not burning more fuel.

In our processes, we could measure pounds of waste sent to a landfill, electricity usage, water usage, fuel usage, and so on. We could then convert these to carbon emissions for a high-level metric. But for the purpose of taking action, it may be better to leave them in their original measurements.

If we define our process outputs (Y) as carbon emissions and waste, using quality tools we can build an improvement project with defined and measurable outputs. And by reducing these, we can have a direct impact on the bottom line.

Having determined what we are going to measure, it is a good time to discuss how we will measure it. The important thing to remember when measuring carbon emissions is that it will be nearly impossible to get an exact measurement without placing monitoring devices on everything that emits carbon. It also is important to remember why we are measuring carbon in the first place. The value of measuring carbon lies in our ability to understand what in our processes emits the most carbon and determine what we can do about it. This is because whenever we are emitting carbon, a resource that costs money is being used. So, any reduction in carbon has the potential to generate savings associated with the reduction. We would like our carbon calculation to be close to the actual and be representative of what we actually emit.

If, for example, we want to determine the carbon emitted from driving to and from work, we can use the miles driven and the average pounds of carbon emitted per mile for cars. Although not exact, this number will be "close enough" for our purposes. As long as the method of calculation is not changed, or the change is identified and understood, it will provide a relative measure of our carbon emissions. It should be noted that if the reporting is done for purposes other than internal improvement, the methods defined by the governing body of applicable standards must be used.

PROCESS IMPROVEMENT TOOLS AND GREEN

It is important to understand the environmental impact of the products you produce or the service you deliver. Many tools that organizations use for process improvement efforts can be applied to understanding the environmental impact as it relates to carbon emissions resulting from your business processes. A process can be broken down into inputs, the process itself, outputs, and what is left over after the product or service is used.

Using standard Six Sigma techniques and defining the output(s) as Y and the inputs as X, we have the notation $Y = f(X)$, where

Y_1 = Total carbon emissions (measured in metric tons)

X_1 = Carbon emissions from fuel burned, electricity used,
    and so on

Y_2 = Waste to landfill (measured in pounds or gallons)

X_2 = Process waste, packaging waste, facilities waste, and so on

A Six Sigma–type project can be built around improving the process inputs (X) in order to reduce the process outputs (Y).

In this case, $Y_1 = f(X_1)$. X_1 are inputs that contribute to carbon emissions. With $Y_2 = f(X_2)$, list inputs that contribute waste to landfills.

The high-level process map shown in Figure 2 represents a typical process and the impacts of that process. This map can be used to develop a more detailed process map for further analysis.

A standard technique used to meet the ISO 14001 requirement of identifying aspects and impacts of activities is called *aspects and impacts analysis* or an *aspects and impacts matrix* (see Figure 3). In this matrix, activities (aspects) that generate potential impacts to the environment or business are listed. The actual impact on the business or environment can be listed in the next columns, and then consequences are evaluated. Typically, you evaluate consequences to the business, legislative requirements, the likelihood of the event occurring, and the impact on the environment should it occur. A rating system is employed, in this case 1 to 5, with 5 being the most significant. The rating for each category is then multiplied to obtain a significance rating for each aspect. Aspects with the highest significance ratings should be addressed first. Also, any aspect that has a legal impact of 5 using this rating system indicates that there is a law or regulation controlling the aspect and it must be addressed regardless of the overall significance rating. Typically, these items are highlighted on the matrix. The purpose of the highlighting is to identify an item that has a low overall rating (lower priority) but has a legal requirement that has to be met, and action that must be taken to avoid legal consequences. All items identified as carbon emitting or waste creating can be identified, and activities planned to reduce the impact of those items.

This analysis will lead to ideas for improvement projects and identify any areas of the business that require immediate attention. Each aspect should be listed, and either a control method determined or project developed to improve performance. The significance rating can be used as a method to prioritize projects. A control plan for the items identified as significant may look like the control plan shown in Figure 4.

To take a more proactive approach and begin to measure our impact in terms of carbon, which may identify areas for further improvement and

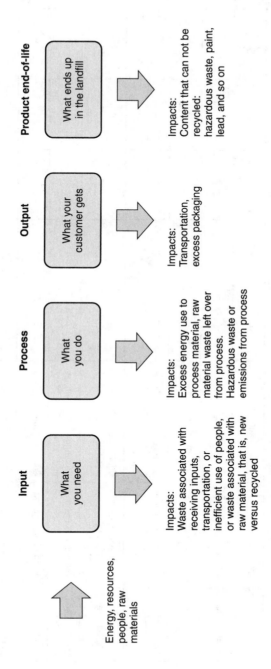

Figure 2   Understanding environmental impact.

Aspect	Business impact	Environmental impact	Business consequence 1 to 5	Legislative impacts 1 to 5	Likelihood 1 to 5	Environmental impact 1 to 5	Significance rating
Office paper	Cost to dispose	Contamination to land (reduction of residual waste)	2	1	5	2	20
Toner cardridges	Cost to dispose	Contamination to land	2	1	5	2	20
Total residual waste	Cost to dispose	Contamination to land	2	1	5	2	20
Fluorescent light bulbs	Cost to dispose/ regulations	Contamination to land	2	5	5	3	150
Solvent cleaning machine	Cost of solvent and disposal	Known ozone depleter, contamination to land and air	2	5	5	3	150
Waste holding area	Cost of hazardous waste disposal regulations	Contamination to land and water	4	5	4	3	240
Storm water management	Permitting regulations	Contamination to land and water	2	5	3	1	30
Fire	Runoff of fire-fighting effort	Contamination to land and water	3	3	1	4	36
Janitorial services	Cost	Contamination to land and water	4	1	5	1	20

Figure 3   Aspects and impacts analysis.

Aspect	Business impact	Environmental impact	Business consequence 1 to 5	Legislative impacts 1 to 5	Likelihood 1 to 5	Environmental impact 1 to 5	Significance rating
Pest control	Cost	Contamination to land and water	3	4	3	2	72
Electrical	Cost	Carbon emissions	2	1	2	2	8
HVAC	Cost/legal (Freon)	Depletion of ozone	3	5	1	4	60
Heating	Cost	Carbon emissions	2	1	5	4	40
Employee commutes	Cost to employee	Carbon emissions	1	1	5	4	20
Paint and thinner waste	Cost to dispose, possible regulations	Contamination to land, water, and air	2	5	5	2	100
Chemical spill	Cost of clean-up	Contamination to land, water, and air	2	3	2	2	24
Cardboard	Cost of material, disposal, and shipping	Reduction of natural resources	2	1	5	1	10
Dunnage	Cost of material, disposal, and shipping	Contamination to land, water	1	1	5	1	5
	Possible regulations	Reduction of natural resources					
Scrap metal	Cost savings from disposal	Reduced contamination to land	1	1	5	1	5

Figure 3   *Continued.*

Aspect	Control and improvement methods
Office paper	Implement recycling program
Toner cartridges	Implement recycling program
Total residual waste	Implement recycling program
Fluorescent light bulbs	Governed by universal haz waste rules. Handled using Haz Waste process
Solvent cleaning machine	Liquid waste a non-hazard. Solid waste a hazard. Both handled using internal procedure
Waste holding area	Waste holding area segregated. Short period of time on site. Spill control measures used
Storm water management	Conditionally exempt. Also have spill control measure in place
Fire	Storm water filter system
Janitorial services	N/A
Pest control	Third-party vendor. MSDS sheets available from vendor
Electrical	Monitor and implement energy savings programs
HVAC	Implement project to reduce energy usage
Heating	Implement project to reduce energy usage
Employee commutes	Implement incentives to car pool
Paint and thinner waste	Third-party disposal. Controlled by internal procedure
Chemical spill	Controlled by containment equipment and internal procedure
Cardboard	Implement recycling program
Dunnage	Implement recycling program
Scrap metal	Scrap metal recycling program

Figure 4 Sample control plan.

additional cost savings, we will investigate a machine shop housed in a 15,000 square foot building located in the northeastern United States.

A tool commonly used to investigate waste in a process, the *value stream map,* will do a nice job as our "carbon stream map" to investigate where waste and carbon may be generated in our process (see Figure 5).

Note: The methods used in the following calculations are intended as a guide to demonstrate how one may calculate carbon emissions. Depending

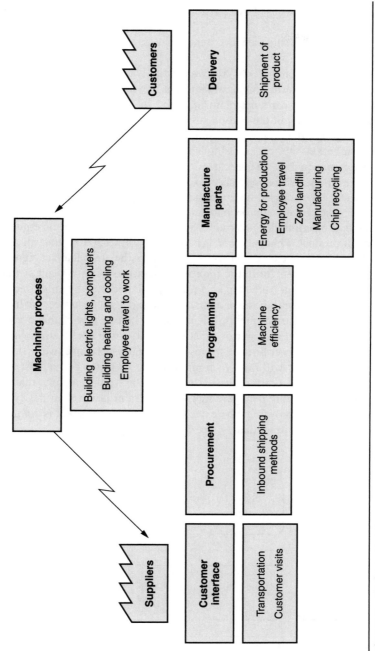

Figure 5 Carbon stream map example.

on the standard that is used in a particular case, the factors and calculation methods may vary.

To better understand the flow of the process, we'll create a process map (see Figure 6).

Now it is a matter of identifying what actually produces carbon or waste at each step, and determining how we might measure it (see Figure 7).

Using both the carbon stream map and the process map may seem redundant. However, in the carbon stream map we look at the flow of the material through the process, and in the process map we look at the flow of the transaction—the order. Using both tools will allow us to gather more ideas for carbon and waste generators.

There are several approaches to calculating carbon emissions. The two that will be discussed here are the *process approach* and the *product approach*. The process approach looks at an overall process and calculates the total carbon emitted. The product approach looks at the carbon emitted per unit of product. This approach is based on the PAS 2050 standard.

The next step in either approach is to identify the areas that are significant and create targets for initial improvement efforts. At this point, actual data may not exist for each step so a ranking method may be employed to help focus on three or four major areas, depending on the resources we have available to make improvements. It is important here to realize that even if the area is not considered significant at this point, it will not be eliminated. We'll just give it a lower priority for resolution. In this example, we will use a ratings matrix that will rank each input from 1 to 10 (10 is the most significant) on impact to carbon/waste. In this model we will assume that all legal and safety requirements are met in the current process. In the event that a situation is discovered where a legal or safety requirement is not met, it must be corrected immediately. See Table 6 for rankings.

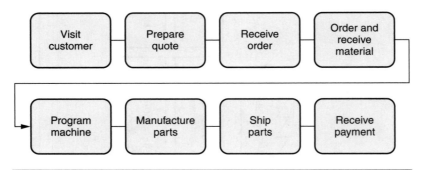

Figure 6   Process flow map example.

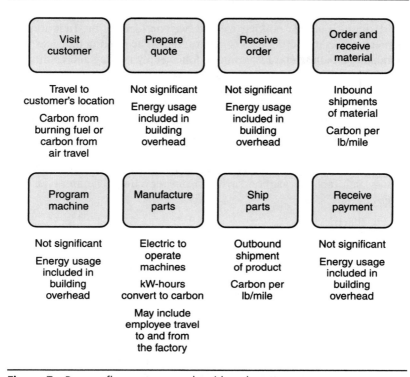

Figure 7 Process flow map example with carbon outputs.

Table 6 Initial ranking.

Input	Carbon/waste generated
Building lighting and computer power	4
Heating and cooling	8
Employee travel	2
Inbound transportation	10
Electric to operate machines	7
Outbound shipments	10
Waste to landfill	3
Waste coolant and machine oil	4

Using this simple ranking method, we can identify the first areas to begin to collect data on, if data is not available. The ranking indicates both inbound and outbound transportation, followed by heating and cooling, as the most significant. If we had available resources to collect data on our entire process, we would not need to use the ranking method shown above. In our example we will take all the activities that are considered significant and calculate carbon emissions for individual activities. Using areas identified in our carbon stream map, process map, and Table 7, we determine the amount of carbon emitted from each activity for the given time period. In this example we will use factors listed in Table 1, carbon emission factors and Table 11, carbon savings from recycling. The areas we will investigate are:

1. Electricity

2. Heating (gas)

3. Employee travel (commutes, air and car business travel)

4. Inbound shipments

5. Outbound shipments

6. Recycling

Carbon emissions are typically reported in metric tons, but these calculations were performed using U.S.ʻpounds. To convert pounds to metric tons, divide pounds carbon by 2204 (2204 pounds/metric ton).

For the example used in this text, we completed the Carbon Emissions Survey Form shown in the Appendix.

Results from our company are shown in Table 7.

Table 7 Survey results.

Electricity	438,037 kW-hours
Gas (building heat)	204,649 cubic feet
Employee commutes	330,000 passenger miles
Employee travel by air	5000 passenger miles
Employee travel by car	56,000 passenger miles
Inbound shipments	12,000 ton-miles
Outbound shipments	5129 ton-miles
Recycling	5000 pounds of paper product

1. Electricity

Our company used 438,037 kW-hours of electricity in the sample year.

Calculate pounds of carbon using factor from Table 1:

$$1.297 \text{ pounds carbon per kW-hr} \times 438,037 \text{ kW-hr}$$
$$= 568,134 \text{ pounds carbon}$$

Convert to metric tons (MT) for reporting:

$$568,134 \text{ pounds} \div 2204 \text{ pounds per MT} = 257.8 \text{ MT}$$

2. Building Heat

The building is heated with natural gas; during the year studied, 204,649 cubic feet of gas were consumed. From Table 1, we see that natural gas contains 0.12 pounds of carbon per cubic foot (CCF).

$$204,649 \text{ cubic feet} \times 0.12 \text{ pounds carbon per cubic foot}$$
$$= 24,558 \text{ pounds carbon}$$

Convert to metric tons for reporting:

$$24,558 \text{ pounds} \div 2204 \text{ pounds per MT} = 11.1 \text{ MT}$$

3. Employee Travel

Employee Commutes. We have 40 employees who commute an average of 33 miles per day. During the year they each made the drive to work 250 times.

Calculate passenger miles:

$$40 \text{ employees} \times 33 \text{ miles} \times 250 \text{ days} = 330,000 \text{ passenger miles}$$

Convert to pounds of carbon, using factor from Table 1.

$$0.7824 \text{ pounds carbon per passenger mile} \times 330,000 \text{ passenger miles}$$
$$= 258,192.0 \text{ pounds carbon}$$

Convert to metric tons:

$$258,192.0 \text{ pounds carbon} \div 2204 \text{ pounds carbon per MT}$$
$$= 117.1 \text{ MT}$$

Employee Travel (Business). Our employees flew a total of 5000 passenger miles on short flights and had 10 nights in hotels.

Flights:

> 5000 miles × 0.5292 pounds carbon per mile (from Table 1)
> = 2646 pounds of carbon

Convert to metric tons:

> 2646 pounds carbon ÷ 2204 pounds carbon per MT = 1.2 MT

Employees also drove 56,000 miles during the year.

Convert to pounds of carbon:

> 0.7824 pounds per mile × 56,000 miles = 43,814 pounds of carbon

Convert to metric tons:

> 43,814 pounds carbon ÷ 2204 pounds carbon per MT = 19.9 MT

Hotel stays:

> 10 nights × 65.11 pounds carbon per night (from Table 1)
> = 651.1 pounds carbon

Convert to metric tons:

> 651.1 pounds carbon ÷ 2204 pounds carbon per MT = 0.3 MT

Total business travel:

> 117.1 MT + 1.2 MT + 19.9MT + 0.3 MT = 138.5 MT

4. Inbound Shipments

To calculate the carbon from inbound shipments we first must determine the weight of the shipments received and the distance the shipments had to travel. This information could be obtained from invoices or the supplier's shipping documents. As with all key areas, if a data collection system does not exist, you may have to create one. For example, during the year 240,000 pounds of aluminum was shipped from a supplier who is 100 miles away. All shipments were made by truck. This data needs to be converted to ton-miles, so first we divide pounds by 2000 to convert to tons:

> 240,000 pounds ÷ 2000 pounds per ton = 120 tons

Since we already have miles, we only need to multiply tons by miles to convert to ton-miles:

> 120 tons × 100 miles = 12,000 ton-miles

This number can then be converted to carbon emissions using the data in Table 1 for truck shipments:

$$12,000 \text{ ton-miles} \times 0.3725 \text{ pounds carbon per ton-mile}$$
$$= 4470 \text{ pounds carbon}$$

Convert to metric tons:

$$4470 \text{ pounds carbon} \div 2204 \text{ pounds per MT} = 2.0 \text{ MT}$$

5. Outbound Shipments

Using the same factor as for inbound shipping, emissions for outbound shipments can be calculated. 624 shipments averaging 40 pounds were shipped an average of 411 miles.

Convert pounds to tons:

$$(624 \times 40) = 24,960 \text{ pounds} \div 2000 = 12.48 \text{ tons}$$

Calculate ton-miles:

$$12.48 \text{ tons} \times 411 \text{ miles} = 5129 \text{ ton-miles}$$

Calculate pounds of carbon using 0.3725 pounds/ton-mile from Table 1:

$$0.3725 \text{ pounds carbon per ton-mile} \times 5129 \text{ ton-miles}$$
$$= 1911 \text{ pounds carbon}$$

Convert to metric tons:

$$1911 \text{ pounds carbon} \div 2204 \text{ pounds carbon per MT} = 0.87 \text{ MT}$$

6. Waste to Landfill

To address the issue of waste (coolant and material sent to landfill), we will not convert this to carbon emissions, but use a direct measure in pounds or gallons of waste. A direct measurement here will be much easier to understand and address. In this case we discovered that the company generated 2400 gallons of waste oil and 6000 pounds of material sent to landfill.

These numbers could be converted to carbon emission equivalents; however, for improvement purposes it may be more meaningful to leave the units in pounds or gallons. This is because reducing waste in pounds or gallons may have more meaning to employees than the number of carbon units.

7. Recycling

Give yourself credit for recycling. Recycling materials reduces the amount of energy required to produce new products from raw materials. The best example of this is aluminum: it only takes about five percent of the energy used to produce aluminum from ore to recycle aluminum.

For every pound of aluminum recycled, the energy saved is equivalent to about 7.5 kW-hours of electricity, or about 0.5 gallons of gasoline (Louisiana Department of Environmental Quality 2010).

For every ton of aluminum recycled, about 10 metric tons of carbon emissions are prevented. So, in this time period our company recycled 60,000 pounds of aluminum chips, which equates to a 300-ton carbon savings (Hutchinson 2008).

Aluminum recycling credit is not included in our summary (see Table 8) since it would not have gone to the landfill in the first place. The aluminum mentioned here is sold as scrap. Depending on the reason for carbon reporting and the scope reported, this may or may not be the case.

For every ton of paper and cardboard recycled, about 2.5 metric tons of carbon emissions are prevented. During the year, our company recycled 5000 pounds or 2.5 tons of paper products for a carbon savings of 6.25 tons of carbon.

To figure our total carbon emissions, we simply add all the emissions and then subtract the carbon savings (Table 8).

Using a Pareto chart (Figure 8), we can easily see the largest contributors to our carbon emissions. The results may vary from what we expected in our initial ratings after we begin to collect actual process data.

The data then can be used as a baseline and drive improvement efforts. The example in Figure 8 was done as an initial assessment; however, the

Table 8   Emissions summary.

Input	Carbon emissions (metric tons)
Electric	257.8
Heating	11.1
Employee travel	138.5
Inbound shipments	2.0
Outbound shipments	0.9
Paper recycling	−6.25
Net emissions	404.05

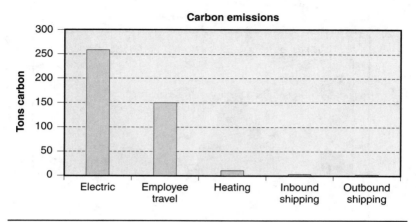

Figure 8 Carbon emissions Pareto chart.

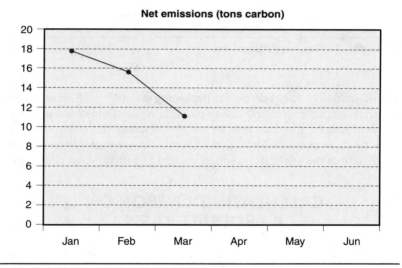

Figure 9 Carbon emissions run chart.

same data could be collected monthly and plotted on a simple run chart to track progress over time. See Figure 9.

In Figure 10, we plot the same data. However, we are using a bar to show total emissions and a line to show net emissions; this allows us to track both total emissions and our recycling effort.

To this point, we have not addressed the question of how to track waste. In this example, the main source of waste will be material sent to the

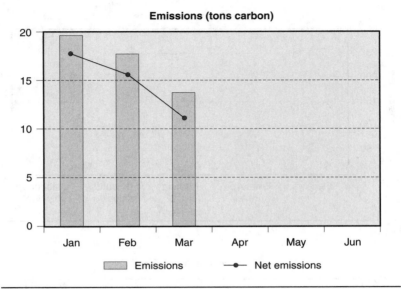

Figure 10 Total and net carbon emissions.

landfill, including waste oil/coolant, packaging material, trash generated by the office, employee lunches, and so on. This waste could be measured in pounds or gallons. Projects could be initiated to reduce this waste and recycle as much as possible. The amount recycled could then be tracked and deducted from the total carbon emissions, just as with recycled aluminum.

CALCULATING CARBON ON A PRODUCT BASIS

The above example investigated carbon emissions using a process approach; in this example we will look at carbon generation per unit of product or service. This method generally follows PAS 2050, but is simplified so the reader can understand the concept.

Using our machine shop, we want to determine the amount of carbon generated per unit of our part number A123-1. First, let's look at a few facts about the product. The part is produced from a piece of extruded aluminum that is purchased from a supplier and shipped to the machine shop. The part is then machined, packaged, and shipped to the customer (see Table 9).

Revisiting the process map for our machine shop (Figure 11), we will begin to allocate carbon emissions to each step of the process.

Table 9   Sample company data.

Raw material weight	12 pounds
Distance from supplier to shop	100 miles
Method of shipping	Truck
Machine time	2 hours
Electricity used by machine	15 kW per hour
Packaged weight of finished product	7 pounds
Distance to customer	700 miles
Shipment method to customer	Truck
People required to produce	2
Percent of building required	10
Percent of office allocated	5
Employee business travel	1 trip and 1 hotel stay

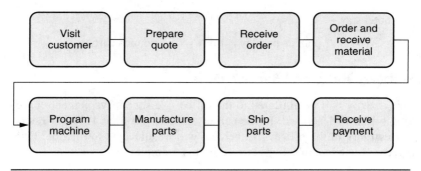

Figure 11   Process flow map example.

In this example, we have received a 1000-piece order from our customer (see Table 10).

Visit Customer

To get this order, we made one 1400-mile round trip by air and spent one night in a hotel. To calculate carbon emissions using factors from Table 1, we have airfare (short flight):

$$0.5292 \text{ pounds per passenger mile} \times 1400 \text{ miles}$$
$$= 740.88 \text{ pounds carbon}$$

Table 10 Machine shop example emissions survey table.

Activity	Pounds carbon
Visit customer—air travel	740.9
Visit customer—hotel	65.1
Prepare quote	71.3
Receive order	22.4
Program machine	31.3
Manufacture parts—machine electricity	38,910
Employee commute	7,886.6
Building heat	181
Shipping	912.6
Total	48,821.2

Our hotel stay:

$$65.11 \text{ pounds per day} \times 1 \text{ day} = 65.1 \text{ pounds carbon}$$

Prepare Quote and Receive Order

This activity will be allocated to the office. We stated five percent of the total office will be used. In the earlier analysis, we used 1100 kW-hours of electricity in the office; five percent will be allocated to this job. Five percent of one month's usage is used in this example:

$$1100 \times .05 \times 1.297 \text{ pounds per kW-hr} = 71.3 \text{ pounds carbon}$$

Order and Receive Material

Ordering material can be included in the above calculation. The 100 pieces at 12 pounds each traveled by truck (0.3725 pounds per ton-mile) 100 miles from the supplier:

$$100 \text{ pcs} \times 12 \text{ pounds} \times 100 \text{ miles}$$
$$= 120,000 \text{ pound-miles} \div 2000 \text{ pounds} = 60 \text{ ton-miles}$$

$$60 \text{ ton-miles} \times 0.3725 \text{ pound carbon per ton-mile}$$
$$= 22.4 \text{ pounds carbon}$$

Program Machine

In addition to the building overhead that has already been calculated, it takes one person one day to program the machine. We will allocate one round trip of this employee's commute to the emissions.

40 miles × 0.7824 pounds per passenger mile = 31.3 pounds carbon

Manufacture Parts

To manufacture the parts, it will take two hours per part for a total of 2000 hours. Four machines will be used, each requiring an operator.

To determine machine electricity:

2000 hours × 15 kW per hour = 30,000 kW-hrs

30,000 kW-hrs × 1.297 pounds per kW-hr = 38,910 pounds carbon

We will also need four machine operators, working eight hours per day:

2000 hours ÷ (8 hours × 4 operators) ≈ 63 days

Employee commutes will include four people for 63 days, traveling 40 miles round trip:

4 people × 40 miles × 63 days = 10,080 miles

10,080 miles × 0.7824 pounds per passenger mile
= 7886.6 pounds carbon

Also, 10 percent of the building was allocated to do this job. During the 63 days, we used 15,000 cubic feet (CF) of gas to heat the building. Ten percent of that is 1500.

Carbon from natural gas heat:

1500 CF × 0.120593 pounds per CF = 181 pounds carbon

Ship Parts

Once manufactured, the parts need to be shipped 700 miles by truck to the customer. Each finished part when packaged weighs seven pounds.

1000 parts × 700 miles × 7 pounds = 4,900,000 pound-miles

4,900,000 pounds ÷ 2000 = 2450 MT-miles

Shipment by truck:

$$2450 \text{ MT-miles} \times 0.3725 \text{ pounds per MT-mile}$$
$$= 912.6 \text{ pounds carbon}$$

Receive Payment

This has been included in the office allocation.

To get our total carbon emissions for the 1000-piece order we have:

$$48{,}821.2 \text{ pounds} \div 2204 = 22.2 \text{ MT}$$

Dividing this by 1000 (number of pieces in the order) gives us carbon emissions per unit:

$$22.2 \div 1000 = 0.02 \text{ MT per unit}$$

This factor could then be used to calculate your total carbon emissions by multiplying carbon per unit by the total number of units produced.

ISO GREEN—IS THIS THE METHOD?

The last thing we need in our busy workday is another "program" to track. By measuring and reporting green efforts in terms of waste and carbon emissions, they can be treated like any other quality or process metrics that are reviewed and managed through the current management system such as ISO 9001 or ISO 14001.

Many organizations utilize the ISO series of standards to manage quality and environmental systems. To the organizations that have these systems in place, incorporating green measures will be a matter of including green metrics and implementing projects that move the company toward becoming green as they have defined it. I feel there is value in using these guidelines within organizations that do not intend to seek certification if no other system for managing the green effort exists.

ISO (International Organization for Standardization) is the world's largest developer and publisher of international standards and comprises a network of national standards institutes from 162 countries (one from each country). There are approximately 17,500 ISO standards currently in publication, and 1100 new ones published every year on a variety of subjects in a range of technical fields. Details of applicable standards are discussed in Section 2 of this book.

The majority of ISO standards are very specific to a particular product, material, or process. But some standards are "generic management system standards" that can be applied to any organization, regardless of its size, its product or service, or its industry segment. They also can be applied whether the entity is privately or publicly held, or a governmental department or agency. Examples of such a standard are the ISO 9001 standard for quality and the ISO 14001 standard related to environmental management. Some of the other ISO standards include:

AS9100—Aerospace

ISO/TS 16949—Automotive

TL 9000—Telecommunications

ISO 26000—Social responsibility

ISO 27000—Information technology

Although these are considered "voluntary" registrations or certifications that can be obtained, many companies are required to obtain these ISO certifications as part of their customer requirements. Certification to a standard also brings a sense of legitimacy to the management system.

So whether we are making efforts to become green or just green*er*, the ISO process may provide a foundation on which to establish a management system.

We'll take a closer look and compare quality methodologies to managing a green process. ISO 9001 defines a set of standard requirements for a management system. These requirements include document control, records control, internal audits, corrective and preventive action, and control of nonconforming material.

When we take the basic requirements that apply to a quality system and apply them to managing green, it is easy to see the application. After all, managing green is much like managing quality.

In managing green, we are really managing our impact on the environment. So, based on the ISO standards, we want to identify the aspects and impacts of our current business on the environment. We then must look at our products, services, or activities to ensure that we have done everything possible to design and produce them in a way that minimizes our impact.

A management system provides a process to manage and improve our business system whether it is related to quality (ISO 9001, AS9100, TL 9000), environment (ISO 14001), or social responsibility (ISO 26000). For our discussions we will utilize the ISO 9001 and ISO 14001 standards to identify how to manage green.

So let's ask ourselves, how will implementing these systems and processes help us become green or greener? We can start by looking at why companies are successful when implementing a management system based on such a standard as ISO 9001 or ISO 14001.

What the standard provides is a solid framework to drive our business and continual improvement processes. Compliance to these standards has typically been up to the quality professionals within the organization. It only makes sense to utilize those skills to also manage the green process. By using the existing quality management system, it is just a matter of introducing and managing green metrics just as quality metrics are managed.

Looking at the major section of the ISO standard, we will investigate how to apply the current system to managing green.

Management Commitment and Policy Statement

Any good quality system starts with *management commitment*. Without commitment from your senior management, you can not succeed in this process. This commitment typically comes in the form of a policy. Most companies have a quality policy; a green policy could be developed or green requirements added to the existing quality policy.

Planning and Development

In quality planning and product development, you ensure that your product and process are designed to meet certain quality requirements. Requirements for green can be added to process or product specifications. For example, it can be specified that all products must be designed to be recycled or designed to be free of hazardous substances. Inputs to determine these requirements may come from the aspects and impacts analysis discussed earlier.

Once we have identified our significant environmental factors, goals can be set to meet our objectives. These goals should be based on our green policy and industry standards such as LEEDS, Energy Star, and ATIS.

The planning and development stage is also a good time to determine to what extent your supply base will be involved in the green effort. Will you require your suppliers to monitor emissions or provide a sustainability report?

Business Process Management

The ISO standards require that a quality system be effectively managed. This means that resources and training must be provided to support the system. In a quality management system, this is controlled by the company's management review process. Training and resource requirements for the green effort can easily be added to this review process.

In addition to providing training and resources, processes and procedures should include environmental requirements that support the objectives set in the green policy.

Monitoring and Analysis

Once the goals are set and procedures modified to meet those goals, a method to monitor progress is required. In a quality system this is accomplished through metrics and periodic audits of the system. Existing audits can be updated or new audits added to assess compliance to green objectives. The current corrective and preventive action system can be utilized when performance does not meet the intended goals.

If measures are defined for green as they are for quality, those measures can be incorporated into the existing quality management system, and many aspects of that system can be used to drive continuous improvement as a green company.

ROAD MAP TO A GREEN ORGANIZATION

Having discussed the various tools used to measure and manage green, we will look at an example of how to become a green organization.

Step 1—Determine What Green Means to Your Organization

The first question that must be answered is why your organization is "going green." It may be as a marketing tool, a requirement of a customer, in preparation for upcoming legal requirements, or just the desire to be a leader in your product line. This decision needs to be made at the highest level in the organization to guarantee support for the effort.

Following are a few questions you should ask yourself before embarking on the process to make your organization greener:

- Why does your organization want to go green?

- What is the benefit to the organization?

- Will you seek a certification for your product or service?

- Will green products open doors to new markets?
- Is this or will it be a customer requirement?
- Who will manage the green process?
- What are the scope and boundaries of your green effort?
- Will you provide sustainability reports?
- Do specific ISO standards apply to your product or service?
- Is there a requirement to design products that can be recycled at the end of their life cycle?

Management commitment to the green process is essential and critical to its success. Green measures should become a part of the company's strategic goals and a part of employee performance measures.

Create an *environmental policy*. Like the quality policy, this document demonstrates and communicates management's commitment to environmental responsibility. This policy must support the reason you are going green.

Step 2—Determine How You Are Going to Measure Green

Determining what to measure and report will be dependent on the answer to your first question—why your organization wants to go green. You may need to report emissions in order to be a member of one of the voluntary carbon reporting groups, such as the Climate Registry or the Carbon Disclosure Project. If this is the case, you will need to adhere to defined guidelines on how to report emissions. Another reason for monitoring emissions is to use it as a way to reduce costs. If this is your goal, you will report emissions in more detail and include more in your report, such as employee commutes and supplier impacts. Including this information will allow you to turn your data into opportunities for improvement by identifying the area of the business with the most environmental impact. If you are reporting to meet the requirements of a customer, they may have guidelines to follow. Determining what to report is very much like determining the type of quality system required for your organization—is it to meet a requirement or to drive improvement? A well-designed system will drive improvement *and* meet customer requirements.

Emission reporting is further defined in one of three scopes: scope one is reporting direct emissions, including emissions resulting from combustion; scope two is reporting indirect emissions, including emissions related to the consumption of purchased electricity, steam, or heating/cooling; scope three is reporting all other indirect emissions not already covered, including employee transportation, business travel, recycling, and emissions resulting from production.

Again, the choice for reporting is dependent on the goal of your organization. Scope one is related to a power generation–type company and captures direct emissions. Scope two reporting relates to all other companies, but only captures emissions associated with consumption. Scope three is the most inclusive and captures many of the areas where cost savings could be realized.

Step 3—Baseline Performance

Baselining your current green performance is equivalent to the process capability studies used by quality professionals. Using measures defined in previous chapters, you should determine how you are performing today against your objectives. For example, what are your carbon emissions? How much waste ends up in the landfill? Can your products be recycled at the end of their life cycles? Pareto analysis to determine the categories causing the largest impact will be the input used to determine improvement projects. See the Appendix for a sample emission survey form. This can be used to develop a survey suitable for your particular organization.

Step 4—Set Goals

Set goals for improvement, and select the projects that will meet those goals. Ask yourself, based on current performance, where do we want to be a year from now? What projects will have the greatest return? What projects will save money? What projects will our customer notice? What projects are easiest to implement?

One of the many tools available to analyze potential projects—a *stakeholder analysis*—may be used at this point. A stakeholder analysis compares impact on and influence of various stakeholders necessary to an organization's success. A cost–benefit analysis may be used, or some type of mathematical-based selection matrix could be employed, to determine the best project to focus on first.

Any project selected must be linked to a strategic objective of the company in order to be successful. The strategic objective can then be turned into measurable objectives, and projects can be initiated to support those

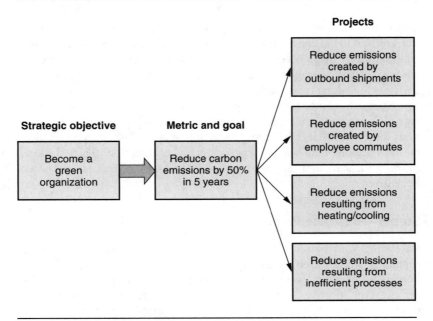

Figure 12 Linking objectives to projects.

objectives. For example, the strategic objective of the company may be to become a "green organization" (see Figure 12).

Once a list of potential projects has been selected, those projects could be prioritized based on benefits and impacts of the project using a project selection matrix. This matrix lists the project along with the benefits of the project, project duration, customer impact, and required investment. Projects with the highest impact rating are selected for action first. Various scales can be utilized in this matrix. In this case, benefits such as carbon reduction and savings are given a rating. The higher the reduction or savings, the higher the number. Ratings for project duration and investment required are just the opposite. The longer the project, the lower the number. Another rating system is used for customer impact. Making a change to internal processes can have either a positive or negative impact on the customer. A project that may have a negative impact is given a rating in the form of a decimal in order to reduce the overall rating and make it less desirable to implement than a project with a higher rating. Figure 13 shows a sample project selection matrix.

Project name	Carbon reduction potential (1 = Low, 10 = High)	Savings (1 = $0, 10 = $1,000,000)	Duration (1 = 12+ months, 10 = <2 months)	Customer impact (0.1 = Negative, 1 = No impact, 10 = Positive)	Investment required (1 = $1,000,000, 10 = $0)	Total project impact rating
Reduce emissions generated by outbound shipments	6	7	2	6	3	1512
Reduce emissions generated by employee commutes	8	2	8	1	2	256
Reduce emissions generated by heating/ cooling	4	5	2	1	3	120
Reduce emissions generated by inefficient processes	6	6	2	5	4	1440

Figure 13   Sample project selection matrix.

Step 5—Educate Employees

Just as employees need to be trained to understand quality principles and tools, they will need training to understand green. There should be overview training to help employees understand why green is important to the organization, and more-specific tools for training of those involved in managing green projects.

Team members who participate on project teams will need training to understand the company goals, the processes used to become green, and the impact of their activities and findings on those goals.

Step 6—Add Green Measures to Performance Measures

Green measures must be made a part of the company's key process metrics, and those metrics must be reviewed at management review meetings. Metrics not meeting the goals require corrective actions to keep projects on track.

Step 7—Manage Projects

Develop an ongoing method to identify opportunities for new green projects. This may be as an input to management review, or opportunities may be reviewed as part of a green steering team. Determine how projects will be managed, tracked, and followed up on. Require teams to report performance to a Champion or green steering team on a regular basis.

Ensure that green metrics are of strategic importance to the organization. Green reporting may also be a customer or legal requirement.

Incorporate green into the design process. Add green questions to the design review process, for example:

1. What are the opportunities to design green into the product?

2. Can all of the product be recycled?

3. Can weight be reduced?

4. Can the product be designed to use less energy or renewable energy?

5. Can products be made smaller or lighter to reduce shipping?

6. Can hazardous substances be removed from the process that produces the product, or the product itself?

7. Can products be designed to last longer and reduce end-of-life impact?

8. Can packaging and transportation distances to the customer be reduced?

Determine to what level your suppliers will be involved and what will be required of your supply base. Will you require your suppliers to be compliant to an environmental or carbon reporting standard, or to meet a sustainability goal?

Step 8—Measure, Report, and Act on Green Metrics

Just as any quality improvement project is not complete until changes are made and controls are in place, a green project will require a fundamental process change and a method to monitor the process to ensure that gains are maintained. This can be accomplished through the creation of a control plan or by making additions to current control plans to address environmental issues. Audits and corrective actions also may be needed to address issues when goals are not met.

There must be a measuring system in place to allow periodic review of performance, particularly if the effort is ISO registered. The place for this may be management review, as discussed earlier. A green or sustainability report may be required to meet a reporting or customer requirement.

It is important to document your work in a *sustainability report.* A sustainability report demonstrates your commitment to the environment in the form of a public record and shows plans and objectives for improving environmental performance. In Wal-Mart's supplier questionnaire, the company asks suppliers if they have set publicly available GHG reduction targets.

The Global Reporting Initiative (GRI) has published guidelines that define the purpose of a sustainability report and outline what it should include. In its sustainability reporting guideline, GRI defines sustainability reporting as "the practice of measuring, disclosing, and being accountable to internal and external stakeholders for organizational performance toward the goal of sustainable development" (Global Reporting Initiative 2010).

The guidelines also address in detail what metrics are considered core in several areas of sustainability, including economic, environmental, labor practices, human rights, and product responsibility. Even if your company does not plan to report to the GRI, the guidelines include many ideas for metrics in each category that may be beneficial. For example, environmental aspects include materials used by volume, direct and indirect energy consumption, energy saved by conservation and efficiency projects, and total water usage.

The GRI reporting guidelines also will be useful to those expanding their green programs to include other sustainability issues in line with ISO 26000. The guidelines list metrics for human rights such as total hours spent on training employees on policies concerning human rights, actions taken on discrimination issues, and incidents involving violations of the rights of indigenous people.

Figure 14 shows an example of what a road map to green might look like.

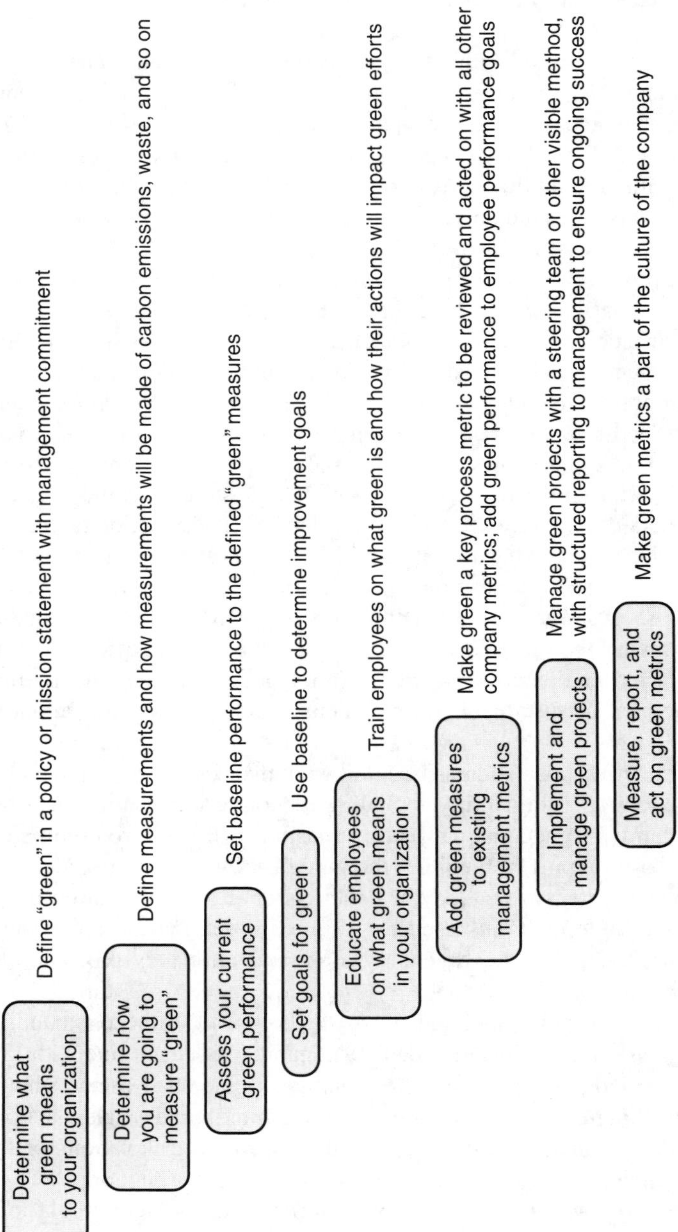

Determine what green means to your organization

Define "green" in a policy or mission statement with management commitment

Determine how you are going to measure "green"

Define measurements and how measurements will be made of carbon emissions, waste, and so on

Assess your current green performance

Set baseline performance to the defined "green" measures

Set goals for green

Use baseline to determine improvement goals

Educate employees on what green means in your organization

Train employees on what green is and how their actions will impact green efforts

Add green measures to existing management metrics

Make green a key process metric to be reviewed and acted on with all other company metrics; add green performance to employee performance goals

Implement and manage green projects

Manage green projects with a steering team or other visible method, with structured reporting to management to ensure ongoing success

Measure, report, and act on green metrics

Make green metrics a part of the culture of the company

Figure 14 Road map to green.

PROBLEMS AND CHALLENGES

There's something happening here
What it is ain't exactly clear
There's a man with a gun over there
Telling me I got to beware
I think it's time we stop, children, what's that sound
Everybody look what's going down
There's battle lines being drawn
Nobody's right if everybody's wrong
Young people speaking their minds
Getting so much resistance from behind
I think it's time we stop, hey, what's that sound
Everybody look what's going down

—Stephen Stills, Buffalo Springfield,
"For What It's Worth"

There are several challenges with green. First and foremost is the rationale for being green. Just the word stirs emotions and creates sharp political divides. This may be due to the theorized cause-and-effect relationship between carbon emissions and global warming. This relationship either exists or does not exist depending on the study you believe. As business professionals, we can not get hung up on this argument while business opportunities pass us by. Like the song says, "nobody's right if everybody's wrong." We will let the politicians and scientists fight that battle.

What does matter is that consumers recognize and reward green businesses, and we *can* do things to reduce energy consumption to save money and resources while also harming the environment less. Given these benefits, going green should be common sense and not political. Just as many activists have turned political issues into laws in the past, business should expect laws to result from the current wave of green thinking. Regulations and additional requirements are often met with resistance, just as EPA air and water laws were when they were introduced. Those initiatives became law, just like the labor laws, and industry survived. In addition, many countries around the world have much stricter environmental controls and recycling laws than the United States, and business survives. Building quality products did not break the American economy, but proved to be an advantage—and then a requirement—to competing in the world market. I would expect the same of green.

Business has a choice. It can do nothing, wait to see what happens, and take the chance of falling behind in the green race, just as American business did with quality, playing catch-up to Japanese products. Or, it can be proactive and do something to positively position itself and take advantage of potential green markets.

The challenge to define green remains. As discussed earlier, this will be a continuous challenge for some time to come. As with quality, it is very difficult to measure green on a broad basis. However, green can be addressed within various industries and organizations. Just as nothing will ever be perfect, nothing will ever be completely green. This is where a standard process for measuring green will be important. Measuring carbon impacts may be the best method available, but these are estimates and may not satisfy those looking for perfect measurement systems.

Like quality, we must determine what green means and work toward achieving it. Quality has many measurements and definitions and was thought to be too expensive to achieve. This assumption proved to be false in quality concerns, and I think in time the same will be true for green.

There is no "one size fits all" cookbook for businesses to become green. It will be up to each organization or industry segment to determine what green means and how it will be measured. Transparency in reporting methods will be important in achieving this. Each business must define what green is, and define how they will measure and report performance to their green objectives.

At this time, the popular approach to becoming green is the measurement and reporting of carbon emissions. The current thinking is that if the emissions are measured, work can be done to reduce those emissions. This is not without its own challenges. At the current time, there are several methods and standards written as guidelines to reporting carbon. Many are very similar in calculating carbon. Where they differ is in what to report. As mentioned in an earlier chapter, Wal-Mart has asked for a specific method from its suppliers. In the absence of such a request, a reporting method that best suits your business should be adopted.

The examples presented in this text are meant as possible approaches to measuring environmental impacts based on tools used by quality professionals to measure, monitor, and improve product and process quality. It will be up to individual companies to decide what tools and standards they ultimately will use.

GREEN EXAMPLES—WHAT COMPANIES ARE DOING

Companies of all sizes are addressing green issues by developing green products, measuring and reporting carbon emissions, and assessing their impact on the environment. As more companies move in this direction, one would only expect more environmental requirements to be placed on companies that do business with the companies that are leading the environmental charge. These requirements may be placed on your company regardless of what laws are passed. Below is a small sampling of what some companies are doing. This list is not intended to be all-inclusive, but provided to give you an idea of what is currently happening and what may be required in the future.

Wal-Mart—Supplier Sustainability

Wal-Mart has prepared a set of 15 questions for suppliers concerning their sustainability. The questions include, "Have you measured your corporate greenhouse gas emissions?" and "Have you opted to report your greenhouse gas emissions to the carbon disclosure project?"

Procter & Gamble

Procter & Gamble has set goals in the area of environmental and social impact. They have established a goal to develop and market at least $50 billion in sales of "sustainable innovation products"—defined as products with an improved environmental profile—and a goal to reduce carbon emissions by an additional 20% per unit of product, with a total reduction of 50% for the decade.

Their goal in the area of social responsibility is to help 300 million children by delivering four billion liters of clean water, preventing 160 million days of disease, and saving 20,000 lives (Procter & Gamble 2009).

Sony—Green Partner Program

Sony offers its suppliers certification to indicate that they have successfully established an environmental management system. Sony requires suppliers to use clean raw materials and processes, and to deliver a clean product. Clean by Sony's definition indicates that the raw material, process, and product are free of environmentally hazardous substances. Sony has set criteria and audits its suppliers to these criteria.

EPA—Environmentally Preferable Purchasing

The EPA has developed a commitment to environmentally friendly purchasing. This program hopes to use the federal government's buying power to create market demand for green products.

Citizens Bank—Green$ense

The FAQ (frequently asked questions) page of Citizens Bank's Green$ense Web site states that switching to electronic payment can save 6.6 pounds of paper, avoid the use of 4.5 gallons of gasoline, reduce wastewater by 63 gallons, and reduce GHG emissions by 175 pounds annually. This is based on an average household that receives 19 bills and makes seven payments per month banking electronically. This calculation includes production and transportation of the paper, delivering checks to consumers, transporting and clearing checks, and preparing monthly statements.

IBM—Green Sigma

IBM created Green Sigma, an industry alliance with companies such as Eaton, Cisco, and Siemens, to better understand solutions for reducing waste. Green Sigma is a process that applies Lean Six Sigma tools to identify and reduce waste and emissions throughout an organization.

Dow—Six Sigma Savings

Dow Chemical, in a report delivered in 2003, demonstrated the successful application of Six Sigma to four green projects, saving money and reducing waste.

Intel—Water Efficiency

At Intel in Israel, water used to cool servers is being used for hot water in showers (Borden et al. 2007).

Home Depot—Green Purchasing

Home Depot has an Eco-Options program that classifies products and allows consumers to identify and select products that have less impact on the environment. The program allows vendors to submit a survey form detailing environmentally friendly information about their products, including life cycle impact and recycling information. The information is reviewed by Home Depot to determine if the product qualifies as an Eco-Option.

IdleAire—Green Innovation

According to its Web site, IdleAire is a privately held company that resulted from a challenge to A. C. Wilson by his brother-in-law, a long-haul trucking contractor. The challenge was to develop a way in which a trucker could park and shut off the engine of his truck, yet remain warm or cool in the modern comforts of home it afforded.

The answer was a new, environmentally friendly product that enables truckers to obtain heat and air conditioning by attaching a hose-like device to the window of their vehicles while parked. The same product also enables high-speed Internet and e-mail access, phone service, satellite TV, and electricity. On the surface, it may not seem so green until you consider that there are about 1.3 million trucks on the road with sleeper cabs, and drivers are required to rest 10 hours for every 11 on the road. When a truck is stopped, the traditional method to heat or cool it and run electronics is to leave the truck idling. Idling a big rig requires about one gallon of diesel fuel per hour. Therefore, 1.3 million trucks idling for 10 hours per day is a lot of diesel (IdleAire 2008).

Ben & Jerry's HC Freezer

Ben & Jerry's, a company that has made a name for itself by being a leader in corporate responsibility, is testing a new type of freezer for its ice cream. Current freezer technology uses hydrofluorocarbon gases (HFCs) to cool products. HFCs are one of the greenhouse gases. According to Ben & Jerry's, its hydrocarbon (HC) freezers are just as effective at cooling, more efficient in using energy, emit virtually no greenhouse gases, and have no impact on ozone depletion (Ben & Jerry's 2008).

Coors—Alternative Fuels

Coors is taking waste from beer production and making about three million gallons of fuel-grade ethanol per year. This is in addition to the company's practice of selling dried leftover yeast as a pet food additive (Miller 2008).

This is just a small sampling of companies and products that have addressed green. Nearly every major company has addressed, or is beginning to address, sustainability in some form.

PROJECT IDEAS

Within an organization, there are numerous opportunities to reduce environmental impact and to save money. A key to maintaining a successful green program is a steady input of projects. These projects could be identified through an employee suggestion program, result from outputs of a management review, or be directed by a steering team set up to lead the green effort.

Listed below are just a few examples of potential opportunities. Generating potential projects may be a way to get employees involved at an early stage in the process of becoming green. Ideas also can come through the use of many of the tools used to identify and solve quality and process problems.

Green Actions

Green Teams. Set up teams to identify and implement projects to reduce waste and emissions. Green teams can function like quality improvement teams or quality circles, depending on the scope of the projects they address.

Green Walks. Do a green walk around your office, production facility, or distribution site to identify opportunities for improvement. Think about where paper can be eliminated, what lights can be turned off, what equipment can be shut down when not in use, and what could be recycled. These green walks can be conducted periodically, much like safety or 5S audits. A 5S audit addresses the five S's that are popular in lean implementations: sort, set in order, shine, standardize, and sustain.

In many cases, simple and often overlooked things have the potential of saving money while reducing environmental impact. The idea of the green walk is to have employees look for opportunities to reduce waste and save money. Some questions they may ask are:

1. How can waste be reduced?

2. What areas of the business use more energy than necessary?

3. Can lights be turned off?

4. Can water usage be reduced?

5. Can less paper be used?

6. What can be reused? Packaging material, pallets, printer paper?

7. Are all disposable items really disposable? Or can they be recycled or reused?

8. Can recycle bins replace trash cans, and employees separate trash to reduce landfill waste?

In regard to the impact of reducing, consider this from Florida Power and Light:

> In the movie *National Lampoon's Christmas Vacation,* how much could the Griswolds have saved by switching their 25,000 holiday lights to energy-efficient LED bulbs?
>
> The Griswolds could have reduced their $2400 electric bill to $400 if they switched to energy-efficient LED holiday lights (Florida Power & Light Company 2009).

Below is a list of potential projects that may be considered by your green team:

1. Switch from incandescent to fluorescent bulbs.

2. Turn off computers at night and when not in use; use motion sensors for lights.

3. Use waste as fuel.

4. Combine shipments.

5. Separate trash from recyclables.

6. Recycle or reuse packaging.

7. Require all suppliers and customers (if possible) to send invoices, packing slips, and other documentation by e-mail.

8. Reduce employee travel, use remote conferences, begin telecommuting.

9. Investigate energy efficiency when buying electronics and other equipment.

10. Reduce water usage by installing low-flow toilets or using rainwater in some manner.

11. Reduce unnecessary employee commutes; encourage ride sharing.

12. Get rid of unnecessary paper and materials.

13. Utilize more natural lighting.

14. Use green cleaning supplies.

15. Replace the water cooler with filtered water.

16. Program the thermostat.

17. Travel green by using the train, if possible, and try to find a green hotel.

18. Stay in for lunch and reduce those extra miles driven.

19. Refuse paper advertising and force suppliers to provide information in a digital format.

20. Get rid of the filing cabinet to save space and paper; scan and file documents electronically.

21. Change filters on HVAC equipment regularly.

22. Purchase items in larger containers to reduce packaging waste.

None of the above examples will save the earth, but they will result in a step in the right direction by showing employees that the company is serious about protecting the environment, not to mention the cost savings that result from reducing waste.

Another idea is to migrate toward digital or no business cards. Your contact information can be sent quickly by e-mail or text, and your contacts will remember you as the one without a business card. I was skeptical of this myself until I saw it in practice, and it turned out to really make an impression. You may have to warm your sales people up to this one, as it changes the long-held ritual of the business card exchange. Eliminating business cards may have minimal environmental impact, but it could result in a significant cost savings from not buying printed business cards.

You also can get employees to think about that extra sheet of paper or trash. You could implement a program much like many state parks where you must leave with everything you came in with. You also could greatly reduce the number of trash cans and only use recycling bins to force people to think about the differences between recyclable material and trash.

Consider reducing the number of printers, or make it more difficult to print. This will force you to use electronic options. Printing may be a habit that some find hard to break.

Reward employees for being green. Several large companies are providing special parking spots or even cash to employees who buy energy-efficient cars.

The key to any green effort is to make green a part of the company culture and encourage employees to participate. Make it easy for them by sharing easily implemented ideas at first. For example, encourage employees to reduce waste by turning computers off at night. This both reduces carbon emissions and saves money. It may not sound like a big deal, but consider a computer that draws 200 watts. There are 8760 hours in a year, so in one year the computer uses 1752 kilowatt-hours of electricity. At about $0.15/

kW-hr, depending on where you are located, that is $262.82/year. Now if you even have only 50 employees, that is over $13,000.00/year. Since only about 25% of the total hours in a year are spent working, there is a potential 75% cost savings available for operating computers—in this case, nearly $10,000. What business would turn down a $10,000 return with no investment required?

RECYCLING—HOW MUCH IMPACT?

Recycling is not a new concept. I remember collecting newspapers for recycling as a boy scout. I would collect newspapers until the garage was completely full, take them to the recycling center, and receive very little money for my efforts. Of course, the real purpose of recycling wasn't to make money. It was to help the environment. But without some sort of motivation such as money, in those days there was not widespread participation.

Today, recycling is much more common. Many materials are recycled, and the average person now has much greater access to recycling. Many counties have curbside recycling programs with weekly pickups in front of homes. Nearly every town has recycling bins that are available for disposing items free of charge.

Estimates of the number of people who recycle in the United States vary widely. Whatever the number is, I think it is safe to say that the easier it becomes to recycle, the more people will do it. According to thegoodhuman.com, 1500 aluminum cans are thrown away every second, and only about 50 percent of cans are recycled. In America alone, enough aluminum cans are thrown away each year to make 8,000 747 airplanes (The Good Human 2009).

Recycling in the context of this discussion will be limited to the impact recycling has on carbon emissions and waste. This will be calculated in a later example. By actively recycling, one can reduce the amount of new resources used and thus lower the amount of carbon an organization generates. Recycling also reduces waste that must be disposed of. Table 11 shows the amount of carbon saved by recycling.

According to a survey conducted by Green Seal, 87 percent of people surveyed said they recycle. However, the EPA states that only about 33 percent of our waste is diverted from landfills. Clearly there is a gap between what people say they do and their behavior (Green Seal 2009).

Recycling can take many forms in business. Many companies have both recycle bins and trash cans to separate landfill-bound material from recyclable material. This will reduce disposal cost in many areas of the company. Normally, recycled material collection is less costly than waste

Table 11   Carbon savings from recycling.

Material recycled	Carbon saved per ton recycled
Aluminum	10 tons
Glass	.34 tons
Paper	2.5 tons
Plastic	1.7 tons

removal, and possibly free of charge. Some recyclable materials can also be sold. A company can also investigate where items such as packaging can be recycled or reused.

Many opportunities exist for organizations to apply home and consumer techniques to reduce waste while saving money.

In an article in *New Orleans City Business,* author Stephen Stuart cites an example where the tallest office building in New Orleans installed a cardboard baler. With the baler in operation, Browning-Ferris Industries (BFI) would pick up the bales for recycling, saving the building $20,000 (Stuart 2000).

CONCLUSIONS

The concept of green as it relates to business is gaining popularity. We are also flooded with information and claims about green and managing our impact on the environment. The focus on green can be seen almost anywhere, from advertising to television shows on the topic. The concept of "be environmentally friendly and green" is being embraced by both consumers and businesses. Just about everyone has some level of understanding that their actions may have some sort of impact on the environment. The real issue for business is that green can mean different things to different groups of people, and although there are many standards and certifications, no one group has a monopoly on what green is or how to measure it. This is evidenced by the many definitions and many attempts to define it. There are ISO standards that define general requirements for environmental management, there are many product-specific standards, there are building standards, and there are ways to measure and report carbon emissions. All of these methods are aimed at managing and reducing the environmental impact of products and services. There is also a marketing element to being green and having green products. It is difficult to watch television or surf the Web without exposure to a company presenting itself as a green or environmentally friendly company.

The problem with green is that a precise and measurable definition of green that is universal to all businesses is difficult, if not impossible, to pin down. This presents both challenges and opportunities for businesses. Without a measurable definition of green, the door is open to interpretation and claims that may or may not be true. This situation is not unlike the situation faced by companies concerning quality, another concept that has no "one size fits all" definition that applies to all businesses. It is easy for a company to say it is a "quality" or "green" company, but what does that really mean?

Just as the quality image of a company has an impact on the company's business, green has the potential to have a similar impact. This impact should at least be understood by the company. This is especially true for small to mid-size companies. Just as requirements for quality are placed on smaller companies by their larger customers, one can only expect the same to be true as larger companies place more emphasis on the environment and having a greener image.

Green is unique to every business, and green must be looked at as a process that must be managed to meet a moving target. Just as perfect quality is impossible to achieve, completely green products and services are impossible to achieve since resources will always be used by businesses to deliver those products and services.

Green and environmental management is further complicated by politics and opinions as to what the goals of becoming green are. For people who do not believe in global warming or that it is caused by humans, the importance of green is entirely different than it is to those who believe otherwise. What businesses must address is that all of these people are consumers and customers. Opinion and politics have shaped business requirements since the beginning of the industrial revolution, and they will continue to impact business in the form of public opinion and laws relating to environmental management.

The opportunity for business is that no matter the politics, most everyone understands that it is important to protect the environment to some level. And that green is not a bad thing. The issues that divide people arise when green interferes with how people and businesses make money. Loggers, oil companies, and chemical companies may be seen by some as the bad guys, but these businesses produce jobs and are important to the economy. Just like anything else, there has to be a balance between making money and protecting the environment. Green is about protecting the environment, and companies are about making money. It would be foolish to think that everyone will stop flying in airplanes or using electricity. To find the balance between using resources and making money, companies must manage and use resources more efficiently. The opportunity here is that managing and driving efficient use of resources will save money, reduce environmental impact, and present a positive and environmentally friendly image of the company.

Just as every company has a unique plan for producing and delivering quality goods and services, a plan can be developed to become a green company. This plan must define in clear terms what is meant by green. Green may mean reducing carbons emissions, developing energy efficient products, or reducing and reusing waste products. The point is that green will have different meanings to different companies and must be managed as a process. The importance of a solid definition of green is that performance toward meeting the goals can be measured, and it will not be seen as lip service but as a true effort achieving a measureable result. The good news is that green can be handled with tools and techniques that are currently used by companies to drive continuous improvement in many areas of the business. This is especially true if green is managed in measurable terms such as carbon emissions, water usage, and waste.

As a company, you may never choose to report carbon emissions or provide a sustainability report. But having a defined process for becoming green has the potential to satisfy customers and save money. And that is what business is all about.

Glossary

aspects and impacts analysis—A process that evaluates process activities (aspects) and identifies the resulting environmental impact.

carbon credits—Offsets purchased or traded to account for emitted carbon, typically measured in metric tons.

carbon dioxide equivalent—A factor used to relate the environmental impact of gases other than carbon dioxide, using carbon dioxide as the basis.

carbon footprint—Total amount of emissions reported relative to the effect of carbon released by a particular activity.

carbon free—Indicating net carbon emissions of zero, typically achieved by offsetting carbon emissions.

carbon offsetting—The process of investing in or donating money to be used for programs designed to reduce carbon emissions or remove carbon from the atmosphere, such as reforestation or the development of renewable energy.

carbon process map—A diagram that lists individual process steps and identifies sources of carbon from those process steps or a diagram that reflects a process that produces carbon emissions.

carbon reporting—The process of reporting carbon emissions to a data collection body for analysis or benchmarking.

carbon stream map—An adaption of a lean tool, the value stream map, to identify areas of a process that produce carbon emissions.

carbon trading—Activity associated with setting a cap on carbon emissions and selling excess carbon units to those who exceed their emissions amounts, thus creating value for units of carbon.

carbon unit—Units in which carbon is measured and reported, typically metric tons (2204 pounds).

control plan—A table that lists environmental impacts and proposed methods to reduce those impacts.

global warming potential (GWP)—The ability of a gas to trap heat in the atmosphere, this measure is used to compare gases with different heat-retaining abilities. Carbon dioxide has a GWP of 1 and is used as the base. Methane, for example, traps and retains about 20 times more heat than carbon dioxide, so methane has a GWP of about 20.

green certification—Process that evaluates a product or service to determine if the product or service meets a predetermined environmental requirement.

greenhouse gas sink—Physical unit or process that removes a GHG from the atmosphere (ISO 14064:2006).

greenhouse gas source—Physical unit or process that releases a GHG into the atmosphere (ISO 14064:2006).

greenhouse gas reservoir—Physical unit or component of the biosphere, geosphere, or hydrosphere with the capability to store or accumulate a GHG removed from the atmosphere by a greenhouse gas sink or a GHG captured from a greenhouse gas source (ISO 14064:2006).

green product—A product that claims a minimal impact on the environment.

greenwashing or **green sheen**—Exaggeration of claims about the green nature of a product.

passenger mile—Typical measure used to calculate carbon emissions for transportation of people by multiplying the number of people by the miles they travel.

ton-mile—Typical measure used to calculate carbon emissions for transportation by multiplying the tons of freight by the miles it travels.

sustainable product or service—Product or service that does not adversely impact the environment or available resources.

Appendix
Carbon Emissions Survey Form

Company name _____

Address _____

Energy Usage

Annual electric usage in kW-hours _____

What is the source of the electricity? (Coal/Oil/Gas/Wind/Hydro/Solar/ Unknown)

(Optional: List electric usage by month)

How is your building heated/cooled?

Oil _____ gallons/year used

Gas _____ cubic feet/year

Electric _____ (Not required if entered above)

Other _____ Units/year purchased

(Optional: List fuel usage by month)

Employee Business Travel

Miles per year travel by car _____

Flights per year _____

Long: 4000+ miles _____

Medium: 1500–4000 miles _____

Short: Up to 1500 miles _____

(Optional: Detail trips by employee with actual mileage)

Employee Commutes

How many employees do you have? _____

What is the average distance each employee travels to work (round trip)
_____

(Optional: List by employee with actual mileage and MPG of car)

Inbound Shipments

(Please complete for each shipping method)

Truck

What is the average number of shipments received each month?

What is the average weight of each shipment?

What is the average distance each shipment travels?

Rail

What is the average number of shipments received each month?

What is the average weight of each shipment?

What is the average distance each shipment travels?

Air

What is the average number of shipments received each month?

What is the average weight of each shipment?

What is the average distance each shipment travels?

(Optional: List actual shipments with weight, method, and distance)

Outbound Shipments

(Please complete for each shipping method)

Truck

What is the average number of shipments each month?

What is the average weight of each shipment?

What is the average distance each shipment travels?

Rail

What is the average number of shipments each month?

What is the average weight of each shipment?

What is the average distance each shipment travels?

Air

What is the average number of shipments each month?

What is the average weight of each shipment?

What is the average distance each shipment travels?

(Optional: List actual shipments with weight, method, and distance)

Recycling

What material is recycled? _____

List pounds per year of each material _____

_____

_____

(Optional: List actual quantity by month and type of material)

Water Usage

Water usage in gallons/year _____

Waste

How many pounds of trash are sent to the landfill per year?

_____

How many gallons of oil/coolant are disposed of each year?

_____

(Optional: List actual quantity by month and type of material)

Bibliography

Aldo Leopold Foundation. 2009. Web site. Available at: www.aldoleopold.org/. Accessed 2009.

ATIS (Alliance for Telecommunications Industry Solutions). 2010. Web site. Available at: www.atis.org/. Accessed 6/15/10.

Ball, Jeffery. 2009. "Six Products, Six Carbon Footprints." *Wall Street Journal.* March 1, 2009.

Ben & Jerry's. 2008. "Hydrocarbon—The New Cool: The Cleaner Greener Freezer." Available at: www.benjerry.com/activism/environmental/hc-freezer/. Accessed 6/16/10.

Borden, Mark, Jeff Chu, Charles Fishman, Michael A. Prospero, and Danielle Sacks. 2007. "50 Ways to Green Your Business." Fast Company Web page. Available at: www.fastcompany.com/magazine/120/50-ways-to-green-your-business_2.html. Accessed 6/16/10.

British Standards Institution. 2009. Web site. Available at: www.bsigroup.com/. Accessed 3/15/10.

Build Green. 2005. Web page. Available at www.buildgreen.co.nz/definition.html. Accessed 7/7/10.

The Carbon Disclosure Project. 2009. Web site. Available at: www.cdproject.net/en-US/Pages/HomePage.aspx. Accessed 6/15/10.

The Carbon Trust. 2009. Web site. Available at: www.carbontrust.com/Pages/Default.aspx. Accessed 6/15/10.

Carbonfund.org. Web site. Available at: www.carbonfund.org/. Accessed 6/16/10.

Chicago Climate Exchange. 2010. "Overview." Available at: www.chicagoclimatex.com/content.jsf?id=821. Accessed 6/15/10.

Citizens Bank. 2008. Green$ense program. "Frequently Asked Questions." Available at: www.citizensbank.com/greensense/faq.aspx. Accessed 6/16/10.

The Climate Registry. 2008. Web site. Available at: www.theclimateregistry.org/. Accessed 6/15/10.

ClimateCare. 2009. "Outstanding Achievement Award for Carbon-Financed Treadle Pump Programme." Available at: www.jpmorganclimatecare.com/about/news/IDEIaward. Accessed 3/15/10.

CNBC. 2010. *Carbon Hunters: Making Money out of Thin Air.* Available at: classic.cnbc.com/id/35872593/. Accessed 6/15/10.

Committee on Trade and Investment. 2003. "Best Practices of ISO 14021." PDF. Available at www.ecodesign-company.com/documents/BestPracticeISO14021.pdf. Accessed 6/15/10.

Dell'Amore, Christine. 2009. "Copenhagen Climate Conference: What You Need to Know." National Geographic Daily News. Available at: news.nationalgeographic.com/news/2009/12/091205-copenhagen-climate-conference.html. Accessed 6/16/10.

Earth Day Network. 2010. "History of Earth Day." Available at: www.earthday.net/node/77. Accessed 2010.

Environmental History Timeline. 2009. Web site. Available at: www.runet.edu/~wkovarik/envhist/. Accessed 2009.

EPA Climate Leaders. 2010. Web site. Available at: www.epa.gov/stateply. Accessed 2009.

European Commission. 2010. "Recast of the WEEE and RoHS Directives Proposed." "Environment" Web page. Available at: ec.europa.eu/environment/waste/weee/index_en.htm. Accessed 6/16/10.

Florida Power & Light Company. 2009. "Top 5 Energy Tips for 2010." Available at: www.fpl.com/news/2007/113007.shtml. Accessed 6/16/10.

Garber, Kent. 2010. "Top 5 Issues at Copenhagen." *U.S. News & World Report.* Jan 6, 2010. Available at: www.usnews.com/news/energy/slideshows/top-5-issues-at-the-copenhagen-climate-conference/6. Accessed 6/16/10.

Global Reporting Initiative. 2010. Web site. Available at: www.globalreporting.org/Home. Accessed 6/16/10.

The Good Human. 2009. "Americans Throw Away 1,500 Aluminum Cans per Second." Available at: www.thegoodhuman.com/. Accessed 6/16/10.

Green Seal. 2009. "2009 National Green Buying Research." Available at: www.greenseal.org/resources/green_buying_research.cfm. Accessed 6/16/10.

Green Seal. 2010. Web site. Available at: www.greenseal.org. Accessed 6/15/10.

The Green Standard. Web site. Available at: www.thegreenstandard.org/. Accessed 6/16/10.

The Greenhouse Gas Protocol Initiative. 2009. Web site. Available at www.ghgprotocol.org. Accessed 6/15/10.

Hutchinson, Alex. 2008. "Recycling by the Numbers: The Truth About Recycling." *Popular Mechanics* (November 13). Available at: www.popularmechanics.com/science/environment/recycling/4291576. Accessed 6/15/10.

IdleAire. 2008. Web site. Available at: www.idleair.com/. Accessed 6/16/10.

International Organization for Standardization (ISO). Web site. Available at: www.iso.org/iso/home.htm. Accessed 6/16/10.

ISO (International Organization for Standardization). 2006. ISO 14064:2006 *Greenhouse gases—Part 1: Specification with guidance at the organization level for quantification and reporting of greenhouse gas emissions and removals.* Geneva: ISO.

ISO (International Organization for Standardization). 2004. ISO 14001:2004 *Environmental management systems—Requirements with guidance for use.* Geneva: ISO.

Louisiana Department of Environmental Quality. 2010. "Aluminum Recycling." Available at: www.deq.louisiana.gov/portal/tabid/2069/default.aspx. Accessed 6/15/10.

Miller, David. 2008. "Beer Brewer Converts Waste into Ethanol." Iowa Public Television Web page. Available at: www.iptv.org/mtom/story.cfm/feature/482. Accessed 6/16/10.

Official Journal of the European Union, Directive 2002/95/EU. Brussels: 2003a.

Official Journal of the European Union, Directive 2002/96/EU. Brussels: 2003b.

Occupational Safety and Health Administration (OSHA), U.S. Department of Labor. 2010. "Safety and Health Topics." OSHA Web page. Available at: www.osha.gov/SLTC/index.html. Accessed 6/16/10.

Procter & Gamble. 2009. "2009 Sustainability Report." PDF. Available at: www.pg.com/en_US/downloads/sustainability/reports/PG_2009_Sustainability_Report.pdf. Accessed 6/16/10.

RoHS. 2010. RoHS home page. Available at: www.rohs.gov.uk/. Accessed 6/16/10.

Schendler, Auden. 2010. *Getting Green Done: Hard Truths from the Front Lines of the Sustainability Revolution.* New York: PublicAffairs.

Smith, Kevin. 2007. "The Carbon Neutral Myth: Offset Indulgences for Your Climate Sins." Transnational Institute Web page. Available at: www.tni.org/report/carbon-neutral-myth-0. Accessed 6/15/10.

Stuart, Stephen. 2000. "Businesses Take Another Look at the Benefits of Recycling Trash." AllBusiness.com Web page. Available at: www.allbusiness.com/north-america/united-states-louisiana/1160193-1.html. Accessed 6/16/10.

TerraChoice Environmental Marketing. 2010. Web site. Available at www.terrachoice.com/. Accessed 6/16/10.

TransFair USA. 2010. "Fair Trade Overview." Available at: www.transfairusa.org/content/about/overview.php. Accessed 6/15/10.

United Nations Framework Convention on Climate Change (UNFCCC). 2009. "Kyoto Protocol." Available at: unfccc.int/kyoto_protocol/items/2830.php. Accessed 2009.

U.S. Environmental Protection Agency (EPA). 2010. Web site. Available at: epa.gov/. Accessed 6/16/10.

U.S. Green Building Council. 2010. Web site. Available at: www.usgbc.org. Accessed 6/15/10.

Wal-Mart. Web site. Available at: www.walmart.com/. Accessed 6/16/10.

Index

A

Alliance for Telecommunications Industry Solutions (ATIS), 33–34
analysis, and monitoring, 63
aspects and impacts analysis/matrix, 42

B

Ben & Jerry's, 10
    HC freezer, 75
Bhopal disaster, Union Carbide, xi, 5
BP plc, xi
British Standards Institution (BSI), 25
Browning-Ferris Industries, 80
BS5750 standard, 8
Bush, George W., 6
business
    examples of green in, 72–75
    how green relates to, 8–10
    impact of environmental performance on, xi
business cards, digital, 78
business process management, 62–63

C

carbon dioxide (CO_2), 15
Carbon Disclosure Project (CDP), 20–21
carbon emission factors, 14
carbon emissions, 72
    calculating
        using process approach, 48–56
        using product approach, 56–60
    measuring, offsetting, and trading, 13–15
    metric for, 40
    reporting, 64–65
    survey form (appendix), 85
Carbon Hunters: Making Money out of Thin Air, 17–18
carbon neutral, xii, 17
"Carbon Neutral Myth, The," 17
carbon offsetting, 16–18
carbon reporting and reduction, significant events in, 5–7
carbon reporting organizations, 19–21
carbon stream map, 46–50
carbon trading, 17, 18–19
Carbon Trust, 20
Carson, Rachel, 4